Science A

REVISION WORKBOOK

Higher

Series Consultant: Harry Smith   Authors: Iain Brand and Mike O'Neill

THE REVISE AQA SERIES
Available in print or online

Online editions for all titles in the Revise AQA series are available Spring 2013.

Presented on our ActiveLearn platform, you can view the full book and customise it by adding notes, comments and weblinks.

Print editions

Science A Revision Workbook Higher	9781447942153
Science A Revision Guide Higher	9781447942146

Online editions

Science A Revision Workbook Higher	9781447942238
Science A Revision Guide Higher	9781447942207

Print and online editions are also available for Science (Foundation), Additional Science (Foundation and Higher) and Further Additional Science.

This Revision Workbook is designed to complement your classroom and home learning, and to help prepare you for the exam. It does not include all the content and skills needed for the complete course. It is designed to work in combination with Pearson's main AQA GCSE Science 2011 Series.

To find out more visit:
www.pearsonschools.co.uk/aqagcsesciencerevision

Cont

 Anything with this Skills sticker is helping you to apply your knowledge.

A small bit of small print
Target grade ranges are quoted in this book for some of the questions. Students targeting this grade range should be aiming to get most of the marks available. Students targeting a higher grade range should be aiming to get all of the marks available.

Grade ranges
AQA publishes Sample Assessment Material and the Specification on its website. This is the official content and this book should be used in conjunction with it. The questions in this book have been written to help you practise what you have learned in your revision. Remember: the real exam questions may not look like this.

A healthy diet

D-C 1 A healthy diet needs to contain the correct proportions of nutrients. If our diet is not balanced, we may gain or lose weight or be malnourished.

The pie chart shows the amounts of different foods needed in a healthy diet.

fat/sugar 7%
meat 12%
fruit and veg 33%
milk/dairy 15%
bread, rice, potatoes, pasta 33%

(a) Which two groups of foods do we need most of?

....

.... *(2 marks)*

(b) Describe what is meant by the term **malnourished**.

.... *(1 mark)*

(c) Explain how a person's diet can cause them to lose weight.

....

.... *(2 marks)*

D-C 2 Children who do not have enough protein in their diet can develop a condition called kwashiorkor.

(a) Use this information to state what type of condition kwashiorkor is.

.... *(1 mark)*

⟩ **Guided** ⟩ **(b)** Describe why protein is needed in the diet.

Protein is used in the body to release .... and to .... *(2 marks)*

On every page you will find a guided question. Guided questions have part of the answer filled in for you to show you how best to answer them.

(c) Suggest **one** food that could be given to children to prevent them developing kwashiorkor.

.... *(1 mark)*

B-A* 3 An adult male needs to gain 2500 kcal of energy from his food each day (a kilocalorie, kcal, is a unit of energy). It is also recommended that men eat no more than 80 g of fat each day.

A man reads this information on the side of a packet of beefburgers.

> **100 g of cooked beefburger contains 300 kcal of energy. Each 100 g contains 21 g of protein, 0.1 g of carbohydrate and 10 g of fat.**

(a) How much cooked beefburger would the man need to eat to meet his daily energy requirement?

....

.... *(2 marks)*

(b) Explain whether this would be a healthy diet for the man.

....

....

Mass = ... g   *(3 marks)*

Controlling mass

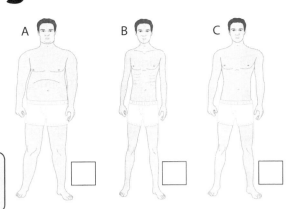

D-C 1 The diagram shows three boys of the same age.

(a) Which boy is likely to have the correct balance between the energy he releases from food and the energy he expends in exercise? Tick (✓) **one** box. *(1 mark)*

A ☐   B ☐   C ☐

(b) Give reasons for your answer.

> Although there are many factors that could have an effect here, you should use the information that you are given in the diagram to explain your choice.

....

.... *(2 marks)*

D-C 2 A drug company is testing a new 'slimming pill'. The company does a trial using three groups of people who want to lose mass.

AQA SKILL Evaluate Page 115

Group 1 follows a low-calorie diet. Group 2 keeps their normal diet but takes the new slimming pill. Group 3 also keeps their normal diet, but the pill they are given is a placebo (it does not contain the new drug).

The scientists measure the change in the mean mass of people in each group over 4 weeks. The data is shown in the table below.

	Mass at start	Mass after week 1	Mass after week 2	Mass after week 3	Mass after week 4
Group 1	70 kg	68 kg	65 kg	64 kg	63 kg
Group 2	70 kg	67 kg	65 kg	64 kg	65 kg
Group 3	70 kg	69 kg	68 kg	69 kg	69 kg

(a) Which group had the largest overall change in mass?

.... *(1 mark)*

Guided

EXAM ALERT

(b) Evaluate the effectiveness of the new slimming pill.

People taking the new pill lost .... mass than people taking the placebo;

but .... mass than those on the low-calorie diet, so the new pill ....

....

> For an 'evaluate' answer, use your knowledge and the information given to consider evidence for and against, and then draw a suitable conclusion from your arguments.

Students have struggled with questions like this in recent exams – **be prepared!**

(3 marks)

B-A* 3 Explain how exercise can help a person to control their weight.

....

....

....

.... *(4 marks)*

Lifestyle and disease

D-C **1** The chart shows how a person's body type is related to their mass and height.

(a) Give the body type of a person who is 160 cm tall with a mass of 60 kg.

....

(1 mark)

(b) An average man is 175 cm tall. What range of mass would be considered normal for an average man?

> Be very careful when reading the scales of this graph. You need to give the lowest and highest masses that are in the normal range for this height.

....

....

(2 marks)

(c) What advice would a doctor give to a man who is 190 cm tall and has a mass of 120 kg? Give a reason for your answer.

....

....

....

(2 marks)

B-A* **2** In 2005, a survey was carried out in New York State. The survey looked at the relationship between people's mass and the incidence of type 2 diabetes.

The graph shows the findings of this survey.

(a) Describe the trend shown by this graph.

....

....

(1 mark)

⟩ **Guided** ⟩ (b) The population of New York State is 19.5 million. Estimate the number of people in New York State who have type 2 diabetes.

The total percentage of people with type 2 diabetes is ....

So, the number with diabetes is .... ÷ .... × ....

Number of people = ... *(3 marks)*

(c) Explain how type 2 diabetes is linked to a person's diet.

....

....

(2 marks)

Pathogens and infection

D-C 1 Ignaz Semmelweis collected data about the numbers of women who died in hospitals after giving birth. He looked at hospital wards served by junior doctors and by midwives.
Here is the data he collected.

	Number of patients	Number of deaths	Percentage of deaths
Doctors who did not wash their hands	20 204	1989	9.84%
Doctors who used a chlorinated hand wash	47 938	1712	

(a) Calculate the percentage of deaths in the ward where doctors used a chlorinated hand wash.

> To calculate a percentage, use the formula: percentage $= \dfrac{\text{number of deaths}}{\text{number of patients}} \times 100\%$

....

Percentage = ... %   *(2 marks)*

(b) What conclusion did Semmelweis draw from the data he collected?

....

....   *(1 mark)*

(c) Give **one** reason why Semmelweis could be confident with the conclusion that he made.

....

....   *(1 mark)*

B-A* 2 Some viruses, such as HIV and measles, are pathogenic in humans.

(a) What is meant by the term **pathogenic**?

> Guided

Something that is pathogenic causes ....

....   *(1 mark)*

(b) Explain how being infected with a small number of particles of a virus, such as the measles virus, leads to illness in a human.

....

....

....

....   *(3 marks)*

(c) Name **one** other type of microorganism that can be pathogenic in humans.

....   *(1 mark)*

(d) Describe **one** way in which pathogenic microorganisms can be transferred from one person to another.

....

....   *(2 marks)*

The immune system

D-C 1 A man had the disease measles as a child. His doctor tells him that he has immunity to the measles virus in the future.

(a) What is meant by the word **immunity**?

.... *(1 mark)*

(b) Describe the steps that take place in order for a person to become immune to a disease.

> You may find the following words useful in your answer: infection, pathogen, antibody, memory, immunity, measles.

....

....

....

.... *(4 marks)*

Guided **(c)** What would happen if the man was infected with the measles virus a second time?

The man would produce antibodies .... and ....

This means that he .... measles.

(3 marks)

D-C 2 One way in which the body can defend itself against pathogens is to produce antibodies. Describe **two** ways in which white blood cells can help protect the body from pathogens.

EXAM ALERT

> Make sure you know the difference between antibody, antitoxin and antibiotic – they sound similar but have very different functions.

> Students have struggled with questions like this in recent exams – **be prepared!**

....

....

....

.... *(4 marks)*

B-A* 3 Each winter, the NHS in England encourages certain people to have a flu vaccine. The vaccine is especially recommended for the elderly and for very young children.

(a) Suggest why young children are recommended for the flu vaccine.

....

.... *(2 marks)*

(b) Many healthy people between 20 and 60 years of age do not have the vaccination. Explain why this group of people still benefit from other people being vaccinated.

....

....

.... *(3 marks)*

Immunisation

D-C   **1**   The graph shows the number of cases of influenza in Australia from 2003 to 2009.

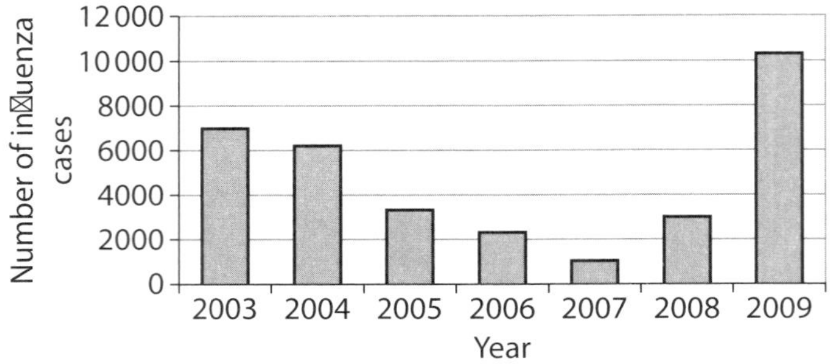

(a) In which year was the number of influenza cases the smallest?

....

(1 mark)

[Graph: Number of influenza cases vs Year (2003–2009). y-axis "Number of influenza cases" 0 to 12000. Bars approximately: 2003 ≈ 7000, 2004 ≈ 6200, 2005 ≈ 3400, 2006 ≈ 2300, 2007 ≈ 1100, 2008 ≈ 3000, 2009 ≈ 10400.]

EXAM ALERT

(b) The number of influenza cases fell from 6200 cases in 2004 to 3400 in 2005. Calculate the percentage change in the number of cases.

> To calculate a percentage change, you need to divide the difference between the readings by the reading for the earliest year, then multiply by 100%.

....

....

Percentage change = ... %

(2 marks)

> You must use the data in the graph to answer this question.

> Students have struggled with questions like this in recent exams – **be prepared!**

(c) Suggest **two** reasons that may explain why the number of influenza cases rose sharply between 2008 and 2009.

....

....

(2 marks)

B-A*   **2**   Young children are given the MMR vaccine against three common viral diseases.

(a) The MMR vaccine contains viral particles. How are these viral particles different from those that cause the diseases?

.... *(1 mark)*

Guided   (b) Explain how the MMR vaccine gives children immunity from disease.

The vaccine stimulates .... cells. These cells then produce

.... If a child is then infected with pathogens for the diseases .... :

.... or .... its body can respond .... *(4 marks)*

B-A*   **3**   Smallpox is a virus that was responsible for millions of deaths every year. However, due to a worldwide vaccination programme, the last case of smallpox in humans was seen in 1977. The World Health Organisation announced two years later that the disease had been eradicated (completely wiped out).

Suggest **one** reason why it is very difficult to get rid of a disease completely.

....

....

.... *(2 marks)*

Treating diseases

 1 A man has a very bad cold. Most colds are caused by viruses. The man asks the pharmacist if he should take some penicillin to help cure his cold. Penicillin is an antibiotic.

 (a) State, with a reason, whether the pharmacist would advise the man to take penicillin.

The pharmacist's advice would be ....

The man's cold is due to a virus, so the penicillin ....

.... *(1 mark)*

(b) Doctors do not prescribe antibiotics for infections such as a sore throat as frequently as they used to 20 years ago. Explain why this is the case.

....

.... *(2 marks)*

2 Some hospitals have problems with a bacterium called MRSA. This bacterium is resistant to many common antibiotics. The graph shows the number of people who died from the MRSA bacterium between 2000 and 2008.

(a) Describe the pattern shown by the graph.

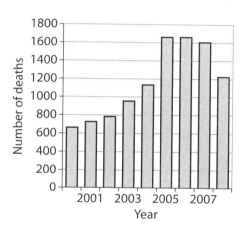

....

.... *(2 marks)*

(b) Suggest an explanation for the shape of this graph after 2006.

....

.... *(2 marks)*

 3 Some strains of the bacterium *E. coli* cause 'travellers' diarrhoea' and food poisoning. The bacterium has shown increased resistance to antibiotics over the past 10 years. Explain how bacteria such as *E. coli* develop resistance to antibiotics.

Remember that antibiotics do not cause bacteria to become resistant, neither does failing to finish a course of antibiotics.

Students have struggled with questions like this in recent exams – **be prepared!**

....

....

....

.... *(4 marks)*

Cultures

 1 Some scientists are testing new antibiotic drugs that they have developed. They soak small discs of blotting paper in solutions of each antibiotic. The discs are then placed on a bacterial growth on a Petri dish. An effective antibiotic will prevent bacteria growing around the disc.

The results of the scientists' test are shown in the diagram.

bacterial growth

antibiotic disc

zone of inhibition (no growth)

(a) Give **two** ways in which the scientists make sure that their experiment is a fair test.

....

.... *(2 marks)*

(b) Which antibiotic is the most effective in this experiment? Explain your answer.

> Remember to use evidence from the experiment to justify your explanation.

....

.... *(2 marks)*

 2 It is important that people doing experiments to culture microorganisms follow some safety precautions. For each precaution given, explain why it is important.

> Guided

(a) The Petri dish is sterilised before being used.

This will .... any microorganisms that are ....

....

.... *(2 marks)*

(b) The inoculating loop is held in a burner before use.

....

.... *(2 marks)*

(c) The lid of the Petri dish is loosely taped down.

....

.... *(2 marks)*

 3 A student is culturing some bacteria. Here are the steps he uses:

- Agar jelly is heated to 80 °C.
- The agar jelly is cooled and a sample of bacteria is added when the jelly is at 21 °C.
- The jelly is put into sterilised Petri dishes and it is then warmed to 25 °C for around 6 hours.

State why each of these steps is important in making the bacterial culture safely and efficiently.

....

....

.... *(3 marks)*

Biology six mark question 1

Note: you need to have studied up to and including page 16 to be able to answer this question.

The diagram shows some cress seedlings that have been growing in a vertical dish as shown.

Always plan what you are going to write for the six mark questions. You are given credit for a well-organised answer.

Students have struggled with questions like this in recent exams – **be prepared!**

The shoots, on the right, have grown one way and the roots, on the left, the other.

Explain how this has happened.

You will be more successful in six mark questions if you plan your answer before you start writing. The question asks you to explain what has happened to both the roots and the shoots so make sure that you include both in your answer.

Here are some points to consider when answering this question:

- what has happened to the roots and the shoots
- the substance in the plant that has caused that response
- what the substance actually does to the roots and what the result is
- what the substance actually does to the shoots and what the result is.

....

....

....

....

....

....

....

....

....

....

....

....

....

....

.... *(6 marks)*

Had a go ☐   Nearly there ☐   Nailed it! ☐

Receptors

D-C 1 Receptor cells in the eye help us to detect objects.

(a) Give the name of the stimulus that activates cells in the eyes.

.... *(1 mark)*

(b) The diagram shows a receptor cell in the eye.

> You need to identify features that are shared by this eye receptor cell and other animal cells. These features will be parts of the cell.

Describe how this cell is similar to other animal cells.

....

....

.... *(3 marks)*

D-C 2 Humans use receptor cells throughout the body to detect stimuli.

(a) Describe how receptor cells in different parts of the body enable us to taste food.

....

.... *(2 marks)*

(b) Receptor cells in the ear allow us to detect sound. Explain **one** other function of the ear.

....

.... *(2 marks)*

B-A* 3 Eight students measure their reaction times in an experiment. Their results are shown in the table.

Student	Boy 1	Boy 2	Boy 3	Boy 4	Mean for boys	Girl 1	Girl 2	Girl 3	Girl 4	Mean for girls
Reaction time in milliseconds (ms)	350	325	335	340		360	320	330	350	**340**

Guided (a) Calculate the mean reaction time for the boys in this experiment.

Mean for boys = (Boy 1 + Boy 2 + Boy 3 + Boy 4) ÷ ....

= ....

Mean reaction time = ... ms   *(2 marks)*

(b) What do these results tell you about the speed that nerves transmit information?

.... *(1 mark)*

(c) The students conclude: 'Boys have a faster reaction time than girls.' Evaluate this conclusion.

....

....

.... *(3 marks)*

Responses

D-C   **1**   A man is changing a light bulb. Suddenly, he gets a shock from the electrical fitting.

(a) Give the name of the structure in the man's skin that detects the electrical shock.

.... *(1 mark)*

(b) When the nervous response reaches the man's spinal cord, it needs to move across a gap from one neurone to another.

    (i) Give the name of this gap between neurones.

.... *(1 mark)*

    (ii) Describe how the nervous impulse travels from one neurone to another.

....

.... *(2 marks)*

▷ **Guided** ▷   (c) Describe the response that would be seen as a result of the impulse in the motor neurone reaching its target.

The impulse in the motor neurone travels to a .... in the man's hand.

This would contract, causing his hand to .... *(2 marks)*

D-C   **2**   Different types of neurone are used to carry information in the nervous system. Two of these neurones are sensory neurones and motor neurones.

(a) State **one** way in which the functions of these neurones are similar to each other.

.... *(1 mark)*

(b) Describe how the functions of these types of neurones are different from each other.

> You need to consider the different targets of these neurones, and therefore the direction in which the impulses travel.

....

....

....

.... *(4 marks)*

B-A*   **3**   A footballer is taking a penalty kick. Explain how the goalkeeper's nervous system enables him to respond to the penalty.

....

....

....

.... *(4 marks)*

Controlling internal conditions

D-C **1** The pancreas produces a substance called insulin. Insulin helps to control the blood sugar levels in the body.

(a) What type of substance is insulin?

.... *(1 mark)*

(b) Suggest what the effect would be on the body if insulin stopped being released.

> A question that asks you to 'suggest' an answer is asking you to apply what you know to the question. Think about what insulin does and why this is important.

....

.... *(2 marks)*

(c) Insulin has its effect on receptors in cells in other organs of the body. State how the insulin travels from the pancreas to these receptors.

.... *(1 mark)*

D-C **2** Sweat contains salts. When we sweat, the ions in these salts are lost from the body. Sweating also helps to control temperature.

Guided

(a) Describe another way in which the body controls ion content.

The body controls the ions lost when .... is excreted.

This function is controlled by the ....

.... *(2 marks)*

(b) Describe how sweating helps control temperature and explain why this is important.

....

....

.... *(3 marks)*

B-A* **3** The recommended daily intake of water is 2.5 litres per day. This water input comes from both our food and drink.

The body loses water through three main processes – through urine and faeces (1.5 litres per day), through sweat (0.7 litres per day) and through one other process (0.3 litres per day).

(a) Identify the process that loses the smallest volume of water and state where it takes place in the body.

....

.... *(2 marks)*

(b) In a typical week, the intake of fluid will differ from day to day. Explain which of the processes of water loss will see the largest percentage change as fluid intake varies over a week.

....

....

.... *(3 marks)*

The menstrual cycle

1 The diagram shows how the levels of different hormones change during the menstrual cycle.

(a) State what happens on day 15 of the menstrual cycle.

....

....

....

(1 mark)

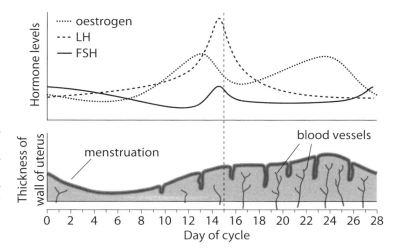

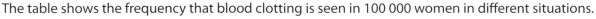

Guided

(b) Describe the role of follicle stimulating hormone (FSH).

The first role is causing .... and the second role is to stimulate

the production of ....   *(2 marks)*

2 Many women take a contraceptive pill to prevent getting pregnant. Like any medication, there are potential side effects of taking 'the pill'.

The table shows the frequency that blood clotting is seen in 100 000 women in different situations.

Situation	Non-smokers, not on 'the pill'	Non-smokers, pregnant	Smokers, not on 'the pill'	Non-smokers, on 'the pill'
Number of women with blood clotting	8	85	100	40

(a) Describe how hormones give 'the pill' its contraceptive function.

....

.... *(2 marks)*

(b) Use the data in the table to evaluate the risk to women who are considering taking 'the pill'.

....

....

.... *(3 marks)*

3 Oral contraceptives can be used to prevent pregnancy. There are two forms of contraceptive pill:
- ones that contain oestrogen and progesterone
- older ones that contain oestrogen only.

Explain how these pills work, and why there are two different forms of these pills.

> Your answer should include the roles of these two hormones on the menstrual cycle. You should also identify, with reasons, which form of pill is less commonly used now.

....

....

....

.... *(4 marks)*

Increasing fertility

D-C 1 In the IVF process, several eggs are removed from the mother and fertilised in a laboratory. One or two of these fertilised eggs are then implanted back into the mother's uterus once they have divided to give a ball of several cells.

(a) Describe how the eggs are fertilised.

....

.... *(2 marks)*

(b) What name is given to the ball of cells implanted back into the uterus?

.... *(1 mark)*

(c) Only one or two of the fertilised eggs are used in the IVF process. Explain why this means that some people are opposed to the IVF process.

In this question, you are asked to give a specific reason why people are opposed to IVF. Remember to think about the information given in the question to help you answer. Other questions will often ask you to present a balanced argument, so make sure you also know reasons in favour of IVF.

....

.... *(2 marks)*

D-C 2 Women who are finding it difficult to conceive a child may be offered fertility drugs to help improve the chance of conception.

(a) Name the hormones that are present in fertility drugs.

....

.... *(2 marks)*

Guided (b) Explain how these hormones help to improve the chance of a woman conceiving a child.

The hormone .... causes .... inside the ovaries.

The hormone .... causes .... from the ovaries.

(2 marks)

B-A* 3 In 2010, 45 250 women underwent IVF treatment in the UK. Of these women, 12 400 were successful in having a child. The cost of a cycle of IVF treatment is £2500.

Use this information, and your own knowledge, to describe the benefits and drawbacks of IVF treatment.

....

....

....

.... *(4 marks)*

Plant responses

D-C 1 The diagram shows a root emerging from a germinating seed.

Guided (a) In which direction will the root grow? Give a reason for your answer.

The root will grow .... because ....

....

.... *(2 marks)*

(b) The growth of the root is influenced by a hormone.

(i) Give the name of this hormone.

.... *(1 mark)*

(ii) Explain how this hormone affects the growth of the root.

> You may find the following words useful in your answer: cell, elongation, accumulation, inhibits.

....

....

....

.... *(3 marks)*

B-A* 2 A teacher shows an experiment to her class. She takes two growing shoots and removes the tip from one of them. She then places the shoots in a box, with a strong light source coming from the right hand side.

The diagrams show the experiment when the teacher has set it up, and after a few days.

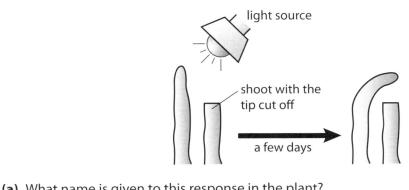

(a) What name is given to this response in the plant?

.... *(1 mark)*

(b) Explain the results of this experiment.

....

....

....

.... *(4 marks)*

Plant hormones

D-C 1 A gardener wants to grow a plant from a cutting. Explain how a substance such as auxin can help the gardener grow a plant from his cutting.

....

.... *(2 marks)*

D-C 2 A woman investigates methods of removing weeds from her lawn. She selects nine areas in her lawn using a 1 m² quadrat. She counts the number of weeds in each quadrat. In three areas, she does nothing to treat the weeds; in three others she removes the weeds by hand; and in three others she uses a chemical weedkiller. She counts the number of weeds again after two weeks.

AQA SKILL
Interpret
Page 115

The table shows the change in the number of weeds in each quadrat.

	Area 1	Area 2	Area 3	Mean
no treatment	+3	+1	+2	
handpicking	−7	−3	−8	−6
weedkiller	−5	−9	−7	−7

(a) Calculate the mean change in the number of weeds for the areas with no treatment.

Mean change = ... *(1 mark)*

Guided (b) When using the weedkiller, the woman noticed that the grass in the lawn was not affected. Give a reason why.

The weedkiller is selective, so it only ....

.... *(1 mark)*

(c) Explain why the woman used a quadrat in this experiment.

....

....

.... *(2 marks)*

B-A* 3 Look at the data in question **2**. The woman concludes from this data that the weedkiller is the best method of controlling weeds. Do you agree? Explain your answer.

> You need to look at the individual data, as well as the mean results, to help to evaluate the conclusion. You should consider the differences between the different treatments and between the different areas.

....

....

....

....

....

.... *(4 marks)*

New drugs

D–C

1 Several different tests are carried out on new drugs before they are released for use. These tests include ones for efficacy and toxicity.

(a) What is meant by the term **efficacy**?

.... *(1 mark)*

> **Guided**

(b) Describe **one** problem with carrying out tests for toxicity of a new drug.

This test is designed to see if the drug is ....

It is unethical to carry this out on .... ,

so .... *(2 marks)*

B–A*

2 In a drug trial, there are usually two groups of volunteers. One group will be given the drug and the other group is given a placebo.

(a) Describe what is meant by the term **placebo**.

.... *(1 mark)*

(b) This sort of drug trial is often set up as a double-blind test. Explain why double-blind tests are often used in drug trials.

> Your answer needs to include information about what a double-blind test is, so that you can say why this approach is so important.

....

....

.... *(3 marks)*

B–A*

> AQA SKILL
> Evaluate
> Page 115

3 Scientists trialled a new drug that was developed to lower blood pressure. They took 1000 people with normal blood pressure (group A) and 1000 people with high blood pressure (group B). Each group was divided in half; half the volunteers were given the new drug and the other half were given the placebo. At the end of the trial, the scientists measured the number of volunteers in each group who had high blood pressure.

The results are shown in the graph.

Bar chart: Number of people with high blood pressure at the end of the trial (y-axis, 0 to 500) versus group. Group A given drug ≈ 15; Group A given placebo ≈ 10; Group B given drug ≈ 110; Group B given placebo ≈ 410.

(a) Explain why it is important for drug trials to use large numbers of volunteers.

....

.... *(2 marks)*

(b) Use information from the graph to evaluate the effectiveness of this drug.

....

.... *(2 marks)*

Thalidomide and statins

D-C   **1**   A drug has been developed to help lower cholesterol in the blood. A study was carried out to test the drug.

200 people took part in the study – 100 people were given the drug and 100 people were not. All the people in the study were given advice on how to lower cholesterol in their diet.

The graph shows the cholesterol levels in the two groups of people over the 13 weeks of the study.

Cholesterol level compared with starting level in %

without statin

with statin

Time in weeks

(a) Explain why the study included a group of patients who did not take the drug.

....

.... *(2 marks)*

(b) What conclusion could be drawn from the results of the study?

> Remember that all patients were given information on how to reduce cholesterol in their diet, so make sure that you take this into account when you look at the data.

....

.... *(2 marks)*

(c) This new drug is a member of the family of drugs called statins. Why is it beneficial to take statins to lower cholesterol in the blood?

.... *(1 mark)*

B-A*   **2**   The following data is taken from a drug trial on a group of men for two different drugs, X and Y, which were developed as sleeping pills.

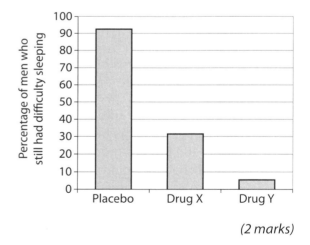

Percentage of men who still had difficulty sleeping

Placebo   Drug X   Drug Y

(a) Describe the relative effectiveness of these two drugs.

Both drugs are ....

than the placebo.

Drug Y is .... effective than

drug X, as .... people

found it effective in treating sleeplessness. *(2 marks)*

(b) Drug Y was marketed under the name thalidomide.

(i) What condition was thalidomide also used to treat, as well as sleeplessness?

.... *(1 mark)*

(ii) Explain why this particular trial would not have highlighted the problems that occurred when thalidomide was used for this second condition.

....

....

.... *(3 marks)*

Recreational drugs

1 In 2006, a group of scientists in Sweden did a study with rats. They took 12 young male rats and gave them small doses of cannabis. After a few weeks had passed, the rats were then allowed to give themselves doses of heroin by pushing a lever.

The scientists found that the rats exposed to cannabis took larger doses of heroin and did so more frequently than rats that had not been exposed to cannabis.

(a) Some newspapers published this story as evidence that cannabis is a 'gateway drug' leading to hard drugs. Suggest **two** reasons why this is may not be true.

> Look carefully at the information that you are given. You need to pick out two reasons why this study is hard to use to make a conclusion about how cannabis use affects people.

....

.... *(2 marks)*

(b) Explain why a drug such as heroin is addictive.

....

.... *(2 marks)*

2 The use of cannabis among young people has become more common over the past 15 years. In 2010, there were over 3700 young people whose use of cannabis led to them needing hospital treatment.

(a) Long-term users of cannabis may notice physical effects on their body. Other than these physical effects, state **one** other effect that cannabis may have on long-term users.

.... *(1 mark)*

Guided

(b) Describe the problems that long-term cannabis users may notice if they try to give up using the drug.

People who have used cannabis for many years may find themselves ....

If they try to give up using the drug, they may have .... *(2 marks)*

3 A recent survey for a BBC documentary found the following information about drug use in the UK.

Drug	Number of users in the UK	Number of deaths in the UK
Cocaine	780 000	214
Ecstasy	500 000	27
Amphetamine	430 000	35

Cocaine and ecstasy are both Class A drugs. The law considers Class A drugs to be the most harmful, and they have the strictest penalties for use or possession. Amphetamines are in the next class down – Class B.

Use the data to decide if this classification is justified.

....

....

....

.... *(4 marks)*

Drugs and health

D-C **1** The graph shows the effect that alcohol has on a person's reaction time. A standard 175 ml glass of wine contains about 1.5 units of alcohol.

> **Guided**

(a) Use the graph to describe the effect that drinking two glasses of wine has on reaction time.

Two glasses of wine contain .... units of alcohol.

This amount of alcohol .... reaction time

by .... milliseconds.

(graph: Reaction time in ms vs Number of units of alcohol, x-axis 0 to 8, y-axis 280 to 420)

(2 marks)

(b) As alcohol can affect the ability of people to drive, there are laws about drinking and driving. Explain how using alcohol would affect the ability of someone to drive.

....

....

(2 marks)

B-A* **2** The graph shows the percentage of adults in the United Kingdom who are smokers, between the years 1980 and 2010.

(graph: Percentage vs Year, y-axis 0 to 40, x-axis 1980 to 2010)

(a) Describe the trend shown by this graph.

....

....

(2 marks)

(b) The population of the UK was 58.8 million in 2000. Use the graph to calculate the number of people in the UK who were smokers in 2000.

....

....

Number of smokers = ... people   *(3 marks)*

(c) It is estimated that the number of heroin addicts in the UK has been fairly constant for many years, at between 250 000 and 300 000.

Evaluate the relative demands that heroin and nicotine place on the National Health Service.

> You need to consider two ideas here – one is how widely each drug is used, and the other is the severity and nature of the effect of each drug on health and, therefore, on the NHS.

....

....

....

....

(4 marks)

Drugs in sport

1 Nasal decongestant sprays often contain a drug called ephedrine. Ephedrine is a stimulant, and it is a banned substance for athletes and those competing in sporting events.

> **Guided**

(a) State how stimulant drugs like ephedrine enhance the performance of an athlete.

A stimulant drug increases ....

(1 mark)

(b) Ephedrine is a legal drug and the nasal sprays are available on prescription. Suggest how this can cause difficulties when monitoring drug use in athletes.

....

.... *(2 marks)*

B-A* **2** Two weightlifters were training to take part in an event. Weightlifter A follows his training plan. Weightlifter B follows the same training plan, but also takes anabolic steroids.

The weight that the two athletes can lift is measured as they train over a 6-week period. This data is shown in the graph below.

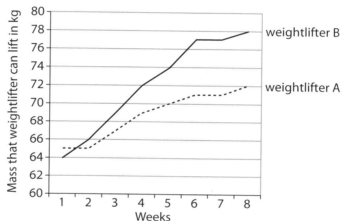

(a) Describe the effect that taking the steroid has on weightlifter B, compared with weightlifter A.

....

.... *(2 marks)*

(b) Explain how the steroid has this effect.

....

.... *(2 marks)*

(c) Although the use of steroids is prohibited in sports, some athletes feel the need to use them. Do you think that athletes can be justified in using steroids? Explain your answer.

> In this question, you are asked to give your opinion on an ethical issue. There is no correct 'yes' or 'no' answer – you should consider the arguments on both sides and then justify the conclusion you make.

....

....

.... *(3 marks)*

21

Biology six mark question 2

Note: you need to have studied up to and including page 31 to be able to answer this question.

The diagram shows cloning in cows. The diagram also shows the technique of embryo transplantation.

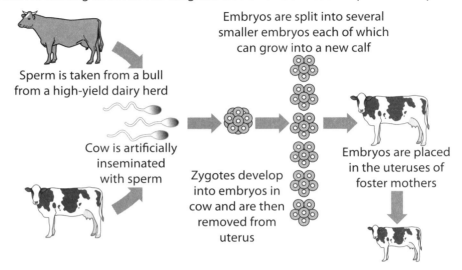

Sperm is taken from a bull from a high-yield dairy herd

Cow is artificially inseminated with sperm

Zygotes develop into embryos in cow and are then removed from uterus

Embryos are split into several smaller embryos each of which can grow into a new calf

Embryos are placed in the uteruses of foster mothers

Using information from the diagram and your own knowledge, compare adult cell cloning with embryo transplantation.

> You will be more successful in six mark questions if you plan your answer before you start writing. The question asks you to make a comparison so make sure you use phrases such as: in this, that happens, whereas in this, something else happens. Make each comparison as you write, not just two separate accounts. It is common for students to get cloning of plants mixed up with that of animals.
>
> Here are some points to consider when answering this question:
> - Point out some similarities between the two processes.
> - Point out some differences between the two processes.
> - Describe the starting point of the process in each case.
> - Describe what treatment the cells undergo.

....

....

....

....

....

....

....

....

....

....

....

....

.... *(6 marks)*

Competition

D-C **1** Meerkats are animals that live in packs and are found in the desert areas of southern Africa. The pack of meerkats is led by a dominant pair of meerkats, known as the alpha male and female.

In this question, you will be asked to think about aspects of the behaviour of the meerkats. Remember to link your answer to the ideas that these animals will compete with each other for resources.

(a) Suggest why younger male meerkats will often try to fight the alpha male.

....

.... *(2 marks)*

EXAM ALERT

(b) When meerkat packs become very large, they often split into smaller packs. The new pack will often move some distance from the original pack. Explain the reasons why a large pack may need to split up.

Make sure that you know what the command words mean. **Explain** means give a reason why. **Suggest** means you need to apply your knowledge to a new situation. **Describe** means say what is happening.

Students have struggled with questions like this in recent exams – **be prepared!**

....

....

....

.... *(2 marks)*

D-C **2** The drawing shows a male peacock.

State **one** adaptation you can see in the peacock and explain why this adaptation occurs.

....

....

.... *(3 marks)*

B-A* **3** The diagram shows a cross-section through a tropical rainforest.

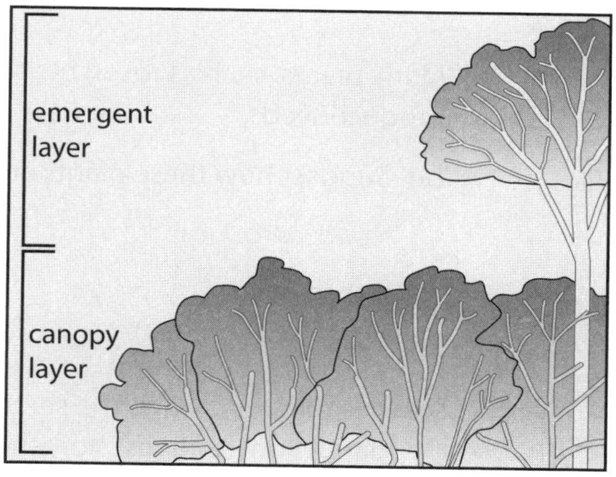

Guided

(a) Some trees are called emergent. They break through the rest of the rainforest canopy. Explain why these trees emerge from the canopy.

The trees emerge through the canopy in

order to get ....

They will also have .... in

order to grow.   *(2 marks)*

emergent layer

canopy layer

(b) The soil in a rainforest is often poor as the minerals are washed away (leached). Suggest how trees in the rainforest may adapt to respond to a leached soil.

....

.... *(2 marks)*

Adaptations

D-C **1** Hydrothermal vents are found on the sea bed. Water that comes out of these vents is often very hot. A species of bacteria survives in this hot water. A variety of other organisms is found nearby.

(a) What name is given to organisms like these bacteria that survive in hostile conditions?

.... *(1 mark)*

(b) Organisms often find it hard to survive on the sea bed, as it is cold and dark.
Explain why there is a large variety of life around hydrothermal vents.

> You should think about what life there usually is on the sea bed, and why the presence of these bacteria makes a difference to other organisms.

....

....

.... *(3 marks)*

D-C **2** The diagrams show two extinct organisms.

EXAM ALERT

Use the features of these two organisms to explain which organism would be better adapted to survive in a cold, polar environment.

....

....

....

....

(3 marks)

dark skin on face   woolly coat   large ears   short fur

wide feet

Organism A   Organism B

> You may be given different examples than these in an exam. Start by thinking of the problems the environment will cause for the organism. Then identify which adaptations help the organism to survive those problems.

> Students have struggled with questions like this in recent exams – **be prepared!**

B-A* **3** Many plants, such as roses, need to attract insects so that the plants can be pollinated and produce seeds.

Guided

(a) Suggest how these plants are adapted in order to attract insects.

Roses produce .... to attract insects.

These have very bright .... to attract insects, and also often

have a strong ....   *(3 marks)*

(b) The diagram shows the seeds that are produced by dandelions. Suggest how these seeds are adapted to make sure that they can be dispersed.

....

....

....

.... *(2 marks)*

Indicators

D-C **1** A student takes two samples of water from a stream. Sample A is taken as the stream passes through fields. The student finds that it contains mayfly larvae. Sample B is taken as the stream passes a factory. Sample B contains bloodworms, as well as mayfly larvae. The student finds information about the organisms present in water in a biology textbook.

Level of water pollution	Indicator species
low	mayfly larvae
high	bloodworms

EXAM ALERT

(a) Use information from the table to state how the student could expect the number of mayfly larvae to be different between the two samples. Tick (✓) **one** box.

> Where a question says 'use the table', make sure you refer to the information in the table in your answer.

☐ The polluted water would have fewer mayfly larvae.

☐ The polluted water would have the same number of mayfly larvae.

☐ The polluted water would have more mayfly larvae.

> Students have struggled with questions like this in recent exams – **be prepared!**

(1 mark)

Guided **(b)** Explain why the organisms found in the water near the factory are different from those found in the clean sample of water.

The factory adds .... to the water in the stream. The water now contains

less dissolved ...., so some organisms cannot survive as well.   *(2 marks)*

D-C **2** Over the last few years, the public in the UK has contributed to a study into the distribution of harlequin ladybirds. This survey has looked at the change in distribution of these ladybirds.

The harlequin ladybird is not native to the UK. It originally came from the hotter areas of Indonesia. The diagrams show the distribution of these ladybirds in 2004 and 2009.

2004   2009

(a) Describe what these diagrams show about the spread of harlequin ladybirds in this time period.

....

....   *(2 marks)*

(b) Some people say that the spread of harlequin ladybirds to the UK is a sign of climate change. Do you agree with this statement? Explain your answer.

....

....   *(2 marks)*

B-A* **3** Describe how scientists can use living organisms to assess air quality.

> Your answer should name an organism that can be used. You should also include information about how scientists relate observations made to the air quality.

....

....

....   *(3 marks)*

Energy and biomass

D-C **1** Deer are herbivorous animals. This means that they feed on grass and leaves.

(a) When the deer digest their food, they use the products of digestion to help supply their energy. What process do deer use to obtain energy from digested food?

....

(1 mark)

Guided

(b) Describe the use that deer have for most of the energy that they transfer from their food.

Deer use this energy to maintain their ....

They also need it for ....   *(2 marks)*

(c) Deer – like all animals – lose a great deal of energy in different ways. Describe **two** ways in which deer lose energy.

....

....

(2 marks)

D-C **2** Groups of organisms in food chains start with an organism called a producer.

(a) Name the **two** types of organism that can be producers in a food chain.

....

(2 marks)

(b) Explain the role of these producer organisms.

┌──┐
│ As this is an 'explain' question, your answer needs to say what these organisms do, and why this is important. │
└──┘

....

....

(2 marks)

B-A* **3** The table shows some information about organisms in a food chain.

Organism	Number of organisms	Mass of each organism	Total biomass in kg
clover plants	10 000	5 g	50 kg
mouse	600	25 g	
snake	10	0.5 kg	

*AQA SKILL
Interpret
Page 115*

(a) Complete the table to show the total biomass for the other organisms in this food chain.

(2 marks)

(b) Draw a labelled pyramid of biomass for this food chain.

(2 marks)

(c) Explain why the total biomass changes from one level to the next in the food chain.

....

....

....

(3 marks)

Decay

D-C

1 A gardener uses compost in the soil of his garden. He then grows tomatoes in the soil.

(a) The compost is made from garden waste. What conditions are needed for compost to form from the garden waste?

To make compost, microorganisms that decay the garden waste need aerobic

conditions, ... and .... *(2 marks)*

(b) Explain why the compost helps the gardener grow tomatoes.

....

.... *(2 marks)*

B-A*

2 In the UK, around 7.5 million tonnes of kitchen waste is produced by domestic kitchens each year. Around 60% of this waste is 'edible waste' – that is, food that is cooked, but not eaten, and food that is thrown away while still edible.

(a) What mass of kitchen waste is edible waste?

....

....

Mass = ... million tonnes *(2 marks)*

(b) A typical landfill site can process 2500 tonnes of waste material per day. Using your answer to **(a)** and your own knowledge, explain why schemes that aim to reduce or recycle this 'edible waste' are so important.

> You should use the data that you have been given here to work out the impact of this waste on landfill sites. Do also think about why this waste, in particular, can be reduced.

....

....

.... *(3 marks)*

B-A*

3 Some scientists investigated the decomposition of leaves. Leaves from the same tree were placed in mesh bags, with different mesh sizes.

The bags were placed in the soil. The bags were removed from the soil every 4 weeks and the mass of the leaves were measured.

The results are shown in the table below.

		0 weeks	4 weeks	8 weeks	12 weeks	16 weeks	20 weeks
Mass of leaves (% of original mass)	**Small mesh**	100	92	84	74	72	68
	Large mesh	100	88	78	66	60	58

Explain the results of this experiment.

....

....

....

.... *(4 marks)*

Carbon cycling

D-C 1 Decomposers play an important role in helping recycle carbon compounds.

(a) Give **one** example of a type of decomposer organism.

.... *(1 mark)*

(b) One source of food for decomposers is dead plants and animals. Name one other source of carbon used by decomposers.

.... *(1 mark)*

(c) Millions of years ago, some organic material did not decompose, but became a source of carbon. State what this source is and describe how the carbon compounds in it are returned to the atmosphere.

> You should be able to identify the carbon-based substances made millions of years ago. You should name the process that will return the carbon to the atmosphere, and name the form in which the carbon will be in the atmosphere.

....

....

.... *(3 marks)*

D-C 2 As part of the carbon cycle, carbon dioxide can be removed from the atmosphere by algae in the sea.

(a) Name the process algae use this carbon dioxide for.

.... *(1 mark)*

⟩ **Guided** ⟩ (b) Explain the importance of this process to the algae.

The algae use the carbon dioxide to make ....

which are used to make up .... *(2 marks)*

B-A* 3 The diagram shows a simple version of the carbon cycle.

Many people are concerned about increasing levels of carbon dioxide in the atmosphere. Use your knowledge of the processes in the cycle to explain whether the processes **in this cycle** are likely to lead to an increase in atmospheric carbon dioxide.

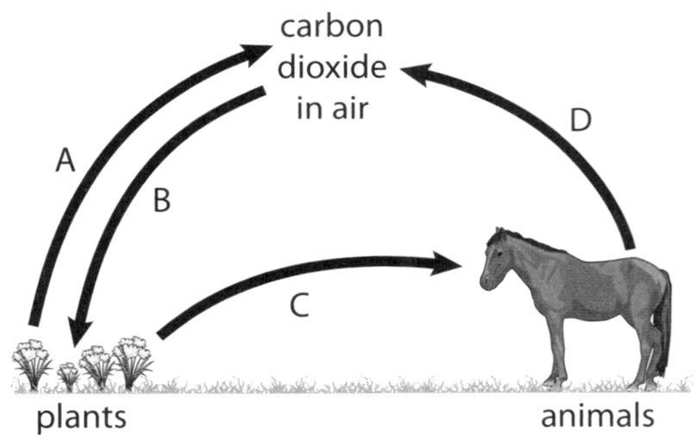

....

....

....

.... *(4 marks)*

Genes

D-C 1 The nucleus of a human body cell contains genetic information on 23 pairs of chromosomes.

(a) State the difference between a gene and a chromosome.

.... *(1 mark)*

> **Guided**

(b) Explain the role of genes in humans.

Genes control how different .... are developed

and .... *(2 marks)*

(c) Describe how genetic information is passed from parent organisms to their offspring.

....

.... *(2 marks)*

D-C 2 A student is studying some sweet pea plants in his garden. He notices that adult plants have different petal colours and different heights to their stems.

(a) What term is used to describe the differences seen in these plants?

.... *(1 mark)*

(b) Describe how parent plants influence the colour of the petals of their offspring.

> You are not expected to go into great detail here – remember this is Science, not Additional Science, so you should limit yourself to saying what the parent plants pass on.

....

.... *(2 marks)*

B-A* 3 Mr and Mrs Johnson have six children. The table shows their heights and the heights of each of their six children when they reached adulthood.

Child	Andrew	Brian	Charles	Dominic	Edward	Francis
Adult height in cm	184	191	173	183	195	169

(a) Calculate the mean height of the six Johnson children.

....

.... *(2 marks)*

(b) Mr Johnson is 190 cm tall and Mrs Johnson is 165 cm tall. Mr Johnson wonders why his children show a range of different heights. Mrs Johnson wonders why the mean height of the children is not the same as the mean height of her and her husband. Suggest an explanation that might answer the Johnsons' questions.

....

....

....

Mean height = ... cm   *(4 marks)*

Reproduction

D-C **1** An amoeba is a single-celled organism.

The diagram shows a parent amoeba with its offspring.

(a) (i) State the type of reproduction shown by the amoeba.

.... *(1 mark)*

(ii) Give **two** reasons for your answer.

You're not asked to give any explanation here – you're only asked to give reasons for your answer. All the information that you need is in the diagram.

....

....

.... *(2 marks)*

(b) How will the genetic information in the offspring compare with that in the parent?

.... *(1 mark)*

D-C **2** Gardeners often grow new plants from cuttings.

(a) The plants grown from cuttings are genetically identical to the parent plant. What name is given to offspring that are genetically identical to the parent?

.... *(1 mark)*

⟩ **Guided** ⟩ **(b)** Describe advantages of being able to grow plants from cuttings.

Plants grown from cuttings have the same .... as the parent plants.

Also, taking cuttings means that the number of plants ....

(2 marks)

B-A* **3** Sexual reproduction is used by humans and other animals to produce offspring. Compare the processes of sexual reproduction and asexual reproduction.

Remember that to 'compare' you should look at both processes equally. You should not just talk about sexual reproduction. You should talk about both sexual and asexual reproduction.

....

....

....

....

.... *(4 marks)*

Cloning

D-C 1 A farmer has grown a carrot that is resistant to attack by insects. He wants to produce more carrots that have the same characteristic.

He does this by taking very small pieces of the carrot plant. He grows these very small pieces into clones of the original carrot plant.

(a) What does the farmer need to make the small pieces of carrot grow?

.... *(1 mark)*

(b) What is meant by the term **clone**?

.... *(1 mark)*

⟩ **Guided** ⟩ **(c)** Each very small piece of plant is called a callus. Explain what happens as the callus grows into a clone of the original carrot plant.

The callus starts as ....

Through the process of ...., they turn into an adult carrot plant.

(2 marks)

D-C 2 Another farmer keeps sheep. She has bred sheep with an excellent meat yield.

She uses a technique called embryo transplanting to produce more sheep. She implants the embryos into several different host sheep.

(a) What name is given to the sheep that give birth to the clones?

.... *(1 mark)*

(b) Describe how the embryo transplanting process works and use this description to say why it is useful to the farmer.

> Your description here needs to give the key steps in the embryo transplanting process and to relate this to the farmer's need to produce the sheep she wants.

....

....

.... *(3 marks)*

B-A* 3 'Snuppy' is the name of a dog that was cloned from an adult dog by scientists in South Korea.

Describe the steps that the scientists would have taken when producing Snuppy.

....

....

....

....

....

.... *(6 marks)*

Genetic engineering

D-C 1   Cotton crops in India are often genetically modified so that the plant produces a toxic substance, known as Bt toxin.

> **Guided**

(a) Why is it useful that the cotton plant makes Bt toxin?

The Bt toxin makes the plant ....

This is useful because the plant will have an increased .... of cotton.

(2 marks)

(b) Describe the steps that are needed to make the cotton plant produce Bt toxin.

....

....

.... *(3 marks)*

D-C 2   Rice is a crop plant that is often genetically modified.

One type of genetically modified rice is called golden rice. It is called golden as it has a gene for the protein beta-carotene inserted, which makes it look yellow. Beta-carotene is needed for humans to produce vitamin A.

AQA SKILL
Explain
Page 115

(a) Explain why golden rice might be useful for countries where people have a poor diet.

....

.... *(2 marks)*

(b) Explain **one** reason why some people are opposed to the production of GM crops, such as golden rice.

> There are different reasons why people do not agree with the growing of GM crops. Here, you are asked to pick **one** reason and explain that. Don't just list all the reasons why people oppose GM crops.

....

.... *(2 marks)*

B-A* 3   People who cannot produce the hormone insulin develop a condition called diabetes. People with diabetes need to inject themselves with insulin. Until recently, insulin extracted from dead pigs was used. More recently, human insulin produced from GM bacteria has been used.

Explain the advantages of using GM bacteria to produce the insulin for treating people with diabetes.

....

....

....

.... *(4 marks)*

Issues with new science

D-C 1 In March 2012, scientists in India announced that they had cloned a rare angora goat. Angora goats produce very high-quality wool.

> **Guided**

(a) Explain why scientists have cloned this type of goat.

These goats are rare, so there are .... in the wild to produce the wool. They wool they produce is of high quality, so ....

(2 marks)

(b) In most countries, there are laws in place to prevent similar cloning experiments being carried out on humans. Give **two** reasons why this type of law is in place.

....

....

(2 marks)

B-A* 2 Scientists researching cures for human diseases often use GM mice. These mice either have genes inserted or the activity of some genes suppressed in order that the mice develop the condition being studied.

Evaluate the use of GM animals in medical research.

....

....

....

(3 marks)

B-A* 3 Early in 2012, the British Science Association asked people in the UK for their views on GM food. People were asked if they were concerned about the use of GM technology to grow food.

AQA SKILL Evaluate Page 115

The results are shown in the pie chart on the right.

How concerned are you about GM food?

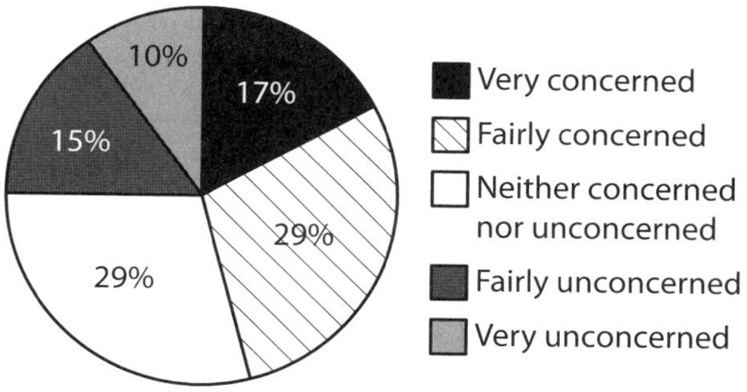

10% / 17% / 15% / 29% / 29%

■ Very concerned
▨ Fairly concerned
☐ Neither concerned nor unconcerned
■ Fairly unconcerned
■ Very unconcerned

(a) Use the data in the chart to suggest whether people in the UK support the production of GM food.

....

....

(2 marks)

(b) Evaluate the use of GM technology to produce food in the UK.

> Your evaluation should consider both advantages and disadvantages of the production of GM foods, before reaching a conclusion.

....

....

....

....

(4 marks)

Evolution

D-C 1 The diagram shows an evolutionary tree.

The arrow coming up through the middle shows the passage of time. Branches from this line show where different organisms evolved in a different way from the ancestors of humans.

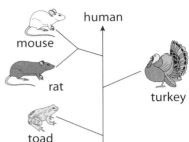

(a) Which of these organisms shares the oldest common ancestor with humans?

.... *(1 mark)*

(b) Give the names of the **two** organisms on this tree that are most closely related.

.... *(1 mark)*

(c) Mice and rats are classified as the same type of animal – they are both rodents. Use the evolutionary tree to justify this decision.

....

.... *(2 marks)*

(d) Suggest how the evolutionary tree supports evolutionary theory.

.... *(1 mark)*

D-C 2 The modern horse is much taller than its ancestors.

⟩ **Guided** ⟩   Explain why the change in height has been an advantage to the horse as it evolved.

EXAM ALERT

A taller horse can see .... more easily.

This means it has more time to ....

.... *(2 marks)*

Organisms do not 'decide' to adapt to their environment. Changes happen due to changes in the genes.

Students have struggled with questions like this in recent exams – **be prepared!**

B-A* 3 Evolutionary changes can happen very slowly by natural selection or slightly more quickly due to mutation.

(a) Describe what is meant by the term **mutation**.

....

.... *(2 marks)*

(b) Explain why natural selection is a very slow process.

....

.... *(2 marks)*

(c) 'All mutations give an advantage to an organism'. Explain whether you agree with this statement.

You should consider what other options exist when a mutation occurs.

....

.... *(3 marks)*

Theories of evolution

 1 One piece of evidence for Darwin's theory of evolution came from studying moths. In the early 1800s, most moths were speckled in colour. This helped them to be camouflaged against trees and so avoid being eaten. Some moths were black and were less well-camouflaged on trees. During the 1800s, air pollution turned trees darker.

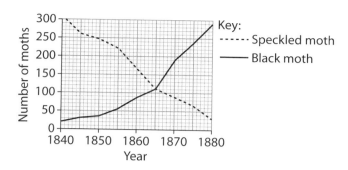

Scientists counted the numbers of speckled moths and black moths over a 40-year period. The results are shown in the graph.

(a) In what year were the numbers of speckled moths and the number of black moths the same?

.... *(1 mark)*

 (b) Describe what the graph shows about the changes in the numbers of both types of moth.

The number of speckled moths goes ....

The number of black moths goes .... *(2 marks)*

(c) In 1880, about 10% of moths are speckled. Suggest **one** reason why the speckled moths do not disappear completely.

.... *(1 mark)*

2 The diagram shows some adult giraffes.

(a) Use Lamarck's theory to explain why theses giraffes have different neck lengths.

....

....

.... *(3 marks)*

(b) Use Darwin's theory to explain why the population of giraffes will change neck lengths over time.

> Your answer should outline the key points of Darwin's theory.

....

....

.... *(3 marks)*

35

Biology six mark question 3

The peppered moth (*Biston betularia*) has two forms. One is dark and one is a light speckled colour. The dark form became much more common during the nineteenth century. One theory suggested that pollution from factories had blackened the tree trunks with soot. The dark moths could not be seen easily by birds. Air pollution is now tightly controlled and the graph below shows how the numbers of dark moths have fallen.

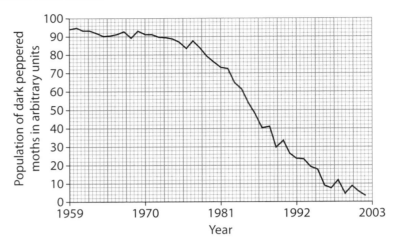

Explain the drop in the number of dark moths using Darwin's theory of evolution by natural selection.

> You will be more successful in six mark questions if you plan your answer before you start writing. The question asks you to explain the fall in the moth population using Darwin's theory of evolution.
>
> Here are some points to consider when you write your answer:
> - What did the moth population look like in the nineteenth century?
> - How has the moth population changed over time? Use data from the graph to help you.
> - What does the theory of evolution say?
> - How does the theory relate to the example given?
>
> To answer the question you need to use this **general** theory to explain the **specific** situation in *Biston betularia*.

(6 marks)

Atoms and elements

 1 Use the Periodic Table on page 112 to help you answer this question.

The symbols for seven elements are listed in the box below.

| Ar | C | Cl | Mg | N | Na | Si |

(a) Give the symbols of **two** elements in the box that will have similar chemical properties.

.... *(1 mark)*

(b) Give the symbol of the element in the box that is in Group 1 of the Periodic Table.

.... *(1 mark)*

(c) Give the symbol for **two** elements, in the first 10 in the Periodic Table, that are in different groups from any of the elements in the above box.

.... *(1 mark)*

> Remember that in the Periodic Table the main groups are the columns numbered 1 to 7 and 0 on the periodic table on page 112. Elements in the same group have similar chemical properties.

 2 (a) Complete the table below with the correct information about the three particles in an atom.

Name of particle	Charge	Where found in atom
proton		
	negative	
		in nucleus

(3 marks)

> **Guided**

(b) A diagram of an atom of lithium is shown on the right.

Describe the structure of this atom, stating the names and number of each particle present.

The lithium atom is made up of a central nucleus containing .... and .... Around the nucleus there are ....

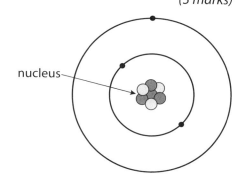

nucleus

> On every page you will find a guided question. Guided questions have part of the answer filled in for you to show you how best to answer them.

(3 marks)

 3 Most materials, both natural and manufactured, are mixtures of different substances. A pure substance will either be an element or a compound. All substances (elements, compounds and mixtures) are made up of tiny particles called atoms.

(a) Approximately how many elements are found naturally on Earth?

.... *(1 mark)*

(b) Describe the difference between an element and a compound in terms of the atoms they contain.

....

.... *(2 marks)*

Particles in atoms

 1 The atomic number and the mass number are used to describe the structure of an atom.

(a) State what each of these numbers tells us about the structure of an atom.

The atomic number tells us the number of .... in the nucleus.

The mass number tells us the number of .... plus

.... in the nucleus. *(2 marks)*

(b) Which of these two numbers is always the same for all atoms of an element?

.... *(1 mark)*

(c) Why do most atoms have no overall charge?

.... *(1 mark)*

 2 Use the Periodic Table on page 112 to help you answer this question.

Complete the information about atomic structure in the table below.

Element symbol	Atomic number	Mass number	Number of	
			protons	neutrons
H	1	1		
			23	28

(2 marks)

 3 Information about four different atoms is shown in the table below.

Atom	Atomic number	Mass number
Atom A	27	59
Atom B	28	59
Atom C	27	62
Atom D	29	63

(a) Isotopes are atoms of the same element that have different numbers of neutrons in their nucleus. Name the two atoms in the table that can be described as isotopes.

.... *(1 mark)*

(b) Which of the atoms has the greatest number of neutrons?

.... *(1 mark)*

(c) State the name of the element for each of the four atoms.

.... *(1 mark)*

B-A* **4** Complete the information about atomic structure in the table below.

Atomic number	Mass number	Number of		
		protons	electrons	neutrons
		17		20
45	96			

(2 marks)

Electronic structure

 1 Complete the energy level (shell) diagrams for the elements with the following number of electrons.

13 electrons   17 electrons   20 electrons

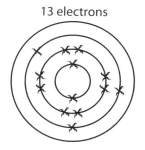   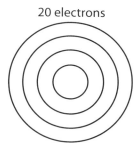

(3 marks)

 2 Use the Periodic Table on page 112 to help you answer this question.

The diagram shows the electron structure of the atoms of an element.

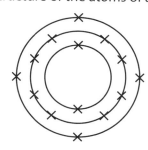

(a) What is the name and atomic number of this element?

.... *(2 marks)*

(b) State the number of protons and electrons in the atoms of this element.

.... *(1 mark)*

(c) What other information is needed to allow us to work out the number of neutrons in the nucleus of the atoms?

.... *(1 mark)*

 3 The electronic structure of magnesium can be written as 2,8,2. Write the electronic structures for the following elements in the same way.

(a) Potassium ....

(b) Phosphorus ....   *(2 marks)*

 4 Complete the missing information in the table below.

Element's name	Lithium	Aluminium	
Atomic number		13	
Diagram			
Electronic structure			2,8

(4 marks)

Had a go ☐   Nearly there ☐   Nailed it! ☐

Electronic structure and groups

1 The electronic structure of an element is shown right.

(a) Which group in the Periodic Table does this element belong to? Give a reason for placing it in that group.

The element is in group 2, as

....

(2 marks)

> You are not expected to learn the electronic structure of the elements in group 2. This question is testing whether you can apply your knowledge of group 1 elements to elements in a different group.

(b) Complete the diagrams on the right with the electron structures of two other elements in the same group as the one above.

(2 marks)

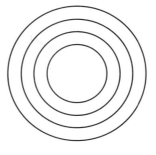
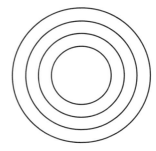

(c) Describe the link between the properties of elements in the same group and their electron structure.

....

....

(1 mark)

2 Use the Periodic Table on page 112 to help you answer this question. The symbols for nine elements are listed in the box right.

C	Co	K	Mg	Na
Ne	Ni	O	Se	

(a) Lithium reacts with water to produce hydrogen gas. Which two metals listed in the box will react in a similar way to lithium with water?

.... *(1 mark)*

(b) Which element listed in the box is a noble gas? .... *(1 mark)*

3 Some information about Group 7 elements, called the **halogens**, is shown below.

Halogen	Atomic number	Melting point in °C	Boiling point in °C
fluorine	9	−220	−188
chlorine	17	−101	−35
bromine	35	−7	59
iodine	53	114	

(a) What happens to the melting point as the atomic number increases?

.... *(1 mark)*

(b) Estimate the boiling point for iodine. .... *(1 mark)*

(c) Under certain conditions hydrogen and chlorine can explode. The balanced equation for this reaction is shown below.

$$H_2 + Cl_2 \rightarrow 2HCl$$

Write a balanced equation for the reaction of hydrogen and bromine.

.... *(2 marks)*

Making compounds

D-C **1** Substances can be classified into two groups, **elements** and **compounds**. The simplest compounds are formed when two elements react together.

(a) Write a word equation for the reaction between iron and sulfur.

.... *(2 marks)*

(b) Describe what happens to the atoms of the elements when they form a compound.

.... *(1 mark)*

D-C **2** The boxes below show the arrangement of atoms in different substances.

(a) Describe how the molecules shown in boxes A and C form and what the bonds are called.

....

....

.... *(2 marks)*

Guided (b) How are the charged particles shown in box B formed and what are they called?

The charged particles are formed by loss and ....

They are called .... *(2 marks)*

B-A* **3** Chlorine forms compounds with several different elements.

Name the compounds formed between chlorine and phosphorus and between chlorine and potassium. Describe how the bonds in these two compounds are formed in different ways.

> The type of bonds formed depend on whether the two elements involved are metals or non-metals. The Periodic Table on page 112 can help you work this out if you do not know.

....

....

.... *(3 marks)*

B-A* **4** Sodium and chlorine react to form the compound sodium chloride.

(a) Complete the diagrams on the right to show the electronic structures of sodium and chlorine atoms.
(2 marks)

(b) Add an arrow to the diagrams to show what happens to the electrons when sodium and chlorine form sodium chloride.
(1 mark)

41

Had a go ☐   Nearly there ☐   Nailed it! ☐

Chemical equations

D-C **1** When calcium carbonate is placed in a test tube and heated strongly, the following reaction occurs.

$$CaCO_3 \rightarrow CaO + CO_2$$

(a) Write a word equation for this reaction.

....   *(2 marks)*

(b) When a 500 g sample of calcium carbonate was heated, 220 g of carbon dioxide gas was formed. What mass of calcium oxide would be left from this sample?

Mass = ... g   *(2 marks)*

D-C **2** The chemical equation for the reaction between methane and oxygen is shown below.

$$CH_4 + 2O_2 \rightarrow CO_2 + 2H_2O$$

(a) Describe this reaction between methane and oxygen in terms of the names of the substances and the number of molecules involved.

....

....   *(2 marks)*

> Guided >   **(b)** When 4 g of methane burns, 11 g of carbon dioxide and 9 g of water are produced. What mass of oxygen was needed to react with the 4 g of methane?

Mass of products = 11 + 9

= 20 g

Mass of oxygen = ... g

> Remember: no atoms are gained or lost during a chemical reaction, so the total mass of reactants used up will always equal the total mass of products formed.

(2 marks)

B-A* **3** Gas burners use methane (CH_4) or propane (C_3H_8) as their main fuel.

(a) Balance this symbol equation for the burning of methane.

CH_4 + ... $O_2 \rightarrow$ .... CO_2 + ... H_2O *(2 marks)*

(b) Balance this symbol equation for the burning of propane.

C_3H_8 + ... $O_2 \rightarrow$ .... CO_2 + ... H_2O *(2 marks)*

(c) Name the products in these reactions.

....   *(2 marks)*

B-A* **4** Sodium metal burns in oxygen to form sodium oxide.

.... Na + ... $O_2 \rightarrow$ .... Na_2O

(a) Balance the above symbol equation for the reaction of sodium and oxygen.   *(2 marks)*

(b) Potassium burns in oxygen in a similar way to sodium.

Write a balanced symbol equation for the reaction of potassium and oxygen.

....   *(2 marks)*

Limestone

1 The Yorkshire Dales is an area of outstanding beauty and an area that was rich in natural resources. Mining for coal, lead and copper has now stopped and no longer spoils the countryside. However, there are still people working in large limestone quarries in the area. Much of the limestone quarried in Yorkshire is transported by road to cement factories in the Midlands.

Guided

Complete the table below to describe one environmental, one social and one economic effect of the limestone quarrying in the Yorkshire Dales. Explain if the effect is positive or negative.

Environmental	Social	Economic
	Quarrying provides work for the local people. This is a positive effect as jobs bring prosperity to an area.	

(3 marks)

2 The flow chart on the right shows the steps in making building materials from limestone.

Name the three solids X, Y and Z.

Solid X is ....

Solid Y is ....

Solid Z is ....

(3 marks)

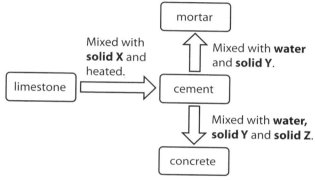

Remember that cement and concrete are different substances.

Students have struggled with questions like this in recent exams – **be prepared!**

3 The table below contains some comparisons of the properties of limestone and concrete.

Property	Limestone	Concrete
appearance	beautiful stone texture, variety of colours	can be stark and bleak-looking
cost	high	moderate
ease of shaping	soft stone, fairly easily shaped, needs stone masons with special tools a lot of waste produced	easily made into complex shapes by moulding but making moulds can be time consuming little waste
hardness	soft	hard
resistance to acid rain	dissolved by acid	acid resistant
effect on environment	obtained by quarrying, no manufacturing processes required	raw materials for concrete obtained by quarrying, cement component requires industrial processing which produces pollution

A builder is considering using limestone or concrete for the walls of a public building. Evaluate the advantages and disadvantages of using these two materials.

....

....

....

....

(4 marks)

Calcium carbonate chemistry

D-C 1 A student used the apparatus shown to investigate the chemical reaction that occurs when copper(II) carbonate is broken down by heat.

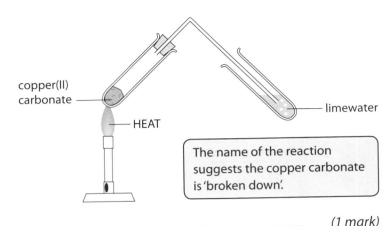

copper(II) carbonate

HEAT

limewater

The student noted that during heating a gas was produced and the copper(II) carbonate changed colour from green to black.

> The name of the reaction suggests the copper carbonate is 'broken down'.

(a) Suggest a name for this kind of reaction.

.... *(1 mark)*

 Guided

(b) Explain how the presence of limewater can tell the student something about the reaction.

If the limewater turns .... then .... has been produced.

(2 marks)

(c) What is the chemical name for the black solid formed during this reaction?

.... *(1 mark)*

B-A* 2 When calcium carbonate is first added to dilute sulfuric acid the reaction forms an insoluble salt called calcium sulfate and two other products.

> Note that the state symbols are given in this equation. Not all balanced equations need to have state symbols.

(a) Complete the following balanced equation for this reaction.

$CaCO_3(s) + H_2SO_4(aq) \rightarrow CaSO_4(s) +$ ....(l) + ...(g)   *(2 marks)*

(b) The reaction starts quickly, but stops after a short time, although there is still calcium carbonate and sulfuric acid left.

Use the above information and your knowledge of chemistry to suggest a reason why this reaction stops before any of the reactants are used up.

....
.... *(2 marks)*

B-A* 3 Some reactions involving calcium carbonate are shown below.

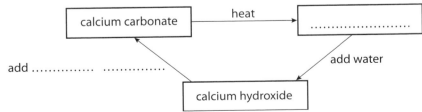

calcium carbonate   heat →   ....

add ....

add water

calcium hydroxide

(a) Write the names of the missing substances in the spaces.   *(2 marks)*

(b) What other name is used to describe calcium hydroxide solution?

.... *(1 mark)*

(c) Calcium oxide is sometimes used by farmers to improve their soil. Suggest what might be wrong with soil that could be cured by adding calcium oxide and state what the calcium oxide would do.

....
.... *(2 marks)*

Chemistry six mark question 1

Metal carbonates decompose on heating to release carbon dioxide gas. You have been asked to design and carry out an experiment to compare the stability of four different metal carbonates.

You are given the following chemicals and apparatus.

Chemicals	Apparatus
calcium carbonate copper carbonate magnesium carbonate zinc carbonate limewater	test tubes stand and clamp test tube rack delivery tube Bunsen burner heatproof mat safety goggles

Describe how you would carry out experiments to tell you which metal carbonates are easiest and which are hardest to break down.

You will be more successful in six mark questions if you plan your answer before you start writing. This is a practical investigation, so think about the following stages:

- the **aim** (what you are trying to find out)
- the **variables** (what you will change and what you will keep the same)
- your **method** (use a labelled diagram)
- **safety** precautions
- your **results** (what you will observe and what you will record).

....

....

....

....

....

....

....

....

....

....

....

....

....

....

....

(6 marks)

Extracting metals

D-C 1 Most metals are found in nature combined with other elements, like oxygen and sulfur. Rocks containing the oxides and sulfides of metals, which are used as a source of the metal, are called ores.

 Guided

(a) Why are gold and platinum never found combined in compounds?

Gold and platinum are never found combined as they are very .... *(1 mark)*

(b) A rock contains a metal. Suggest **one** possible reason why this rock might not be useful as an ore.

.... *(1 mark)*

D-C 2 The date when a particular metal was discovered depends on a number of factors. These include its abundance, the concentration of the ore and the method needed to extract it from the ore. Suggest a reason for the following facts.

(a) The Bronze Age started well before the Iron Age. (Bronze is an alloy of copper and tin.)

....

.... *(1 mark)*

(b) Aluminium is the most abundant metal in the Earth's crust, but it was not discovered until 1825.

....

.... *(2 marks)*

B-A* 3 Metals need to be extracted from their ores. This can be done by heating with carbon or by electrolysis.

(a) Name the type of reaction that extracts metals from their ores.

.... *(1 mark)*

(b) The balanced equation for the reaction between iron oxide and carbon in a blast furnace is shown below.

$$2Fe_2O_3 + 3C \rightarrow 4Fe + 3CO_2$$

Use the equation to describe the reaction, and name the substances involved.

....

.... *(2 marks)*

B-A* 4 The diagram shows the electrolysis of molten aluminium oxide.

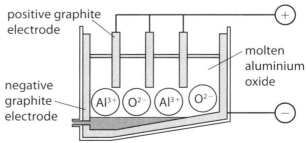

(a) State at which electrode the aluminium will be formed. .... *(1 mark)*

(b) What will be formed at the other electrode? .... *(1 mark)*

Extracting copper

1 **(a)** Scrap iron can be used to extract copper from copper chloride solution. Explain why this is possible.

Iron is more reactive than copper ....

.... *(2 marks)*

The chemical equation for the reaction between iron and copper(II) chloride is shown below.

$$Fe(s) + CuCl_2(aq) \rightarrow Cu(s) + FeCl_2(aq)$$

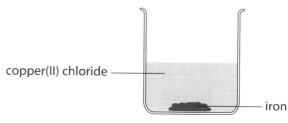

copper(II) chloride —

— iron

(b) Write a word equation for this reaction.

.... *(2 marks)*

(c) What is this kind of reaction called?

.... *(1 mark)*

(d) What solution would be formed if zinc was used instead of iron in this reaction?

.... *(1 mark)*

(e) Suggest why scrap iron is used in the extraction of copper, rather than a more reactive scrap metal such as zinc.

.... *(1 mark)*

2 The increasing use of lower grade metal ores has encouraged scientists to look at new methods of extracting metals.

(a) Why do we now have to use more lower grade ores as sources of metals like copper?

....
.... *(1 mark)*

(b) Describe how the new methods of bioleaching and phytomining can be used to extract metals.

When explaining a process plan your answer to include a description of what, where and how the change is taking place.

....
....
....
.... *(4 marks)*

(c) **(i)** Describe **one** advantage of using bioleaching or phytomining to obtain copper.

.... *(1 mark)*

(ii) Suggest **one** disadvantage of using bioleaching or phytomining to obtain copper.

.... *(1 mark)*

Recycling metals

D-C 1 Much of the metal we use is recycled.

(a) Why does the recycling of metals make our resources of metal ores last longer?

.... *(1 mark)*

(b) Suggest **one** reason why recycling more metals helps improve our environment.

.... *(1 mark)*

B-A* 2 The bar chart shows information about the proportion of different metals that are recycled.

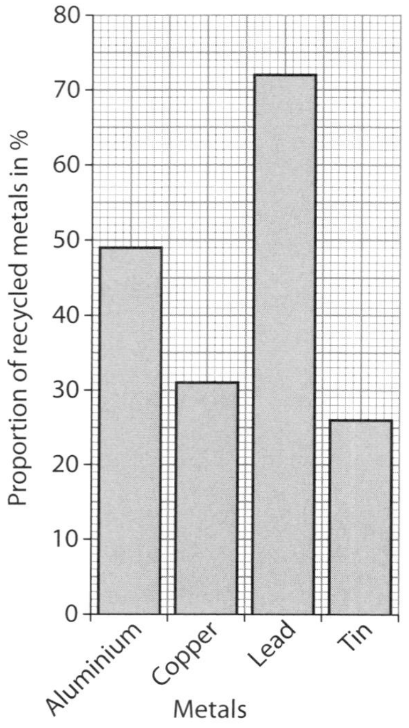

(a) Which **two** metals have the highest proportion recycled?

.... *(1 mark)*

> **Guided**

(b) Suggest **two** reasons why one metal might be recycled more than another metal.

1. Because its ore might be ....

2. Because it might be ....
    to extract the metal. *(2 marks)*

(c) In 2010 the total world lead consumption was approximately 4.6 million tonnes.
    Use this information and the data from the chart to calculate the mass of lead recycled that year.

....

Mass of lead recycled = ... tonnes

(2 marks)

(d) Describe **three** advantages of recycling metals.

....

....

.... *(3 marks)*

B-A* 3 The flow chart shows the main stages in the production of aluminium metal from its ore.

| **Stage 1** Mining bauxite aluminium ore | ⇨ | **Stage 2** Remove impurities | ⇨ | **Stage 3** Processing ore | ⇨ | **Stage 4** Electrolysis of molten ore | ⇨ | **Stage 5** Aluminium run off and casting |

(a) Describe how stages 1 and 2 might damage our environment.

....

.... *(2 marks)*

(b) State **two** costs involved that would make stage 4 the most expensive.

....

.... *(2 marks)*

Steel and other alloys

D-C **1** Steels are alloys of carbon that contain varying amounts of carbon and other metals.

The table below shows how the carbon content affects some of the properties of steel.
(Scale used: * = low and ***** = high)

Carbon content in %	Corrosion resistance	Strength	Hardness
0.0 to 0.1	**	*****	**
0.2 to 0.4	**	****	**
0.5 to 0.8	**	***	***
0.9 to 1.4	**	**	*****

(a) Use the information in the table to describe how these three properties of steel change with carbon content.

....

....

.... *(3 marks)*

(b) Suggest **two** important properties for the steel used for the springs in a car's suspension system.

.... *(2 marks)*

B-A* **2** Iron is extracted from its ore in a **blast furnace**. The raw materials for the process, **iron ore**, **limestone** and **coke**, are fed into the top while blasts of **hot air** are blown in at the bottom of the furnace. The limestone helps remove impurities in the ore. The coke is mainly carbon. Some of the carbon burns to produce the heat needed for the reaction, and some is used to reduce the ore by combining with the oxygen in the **iron oxide**. Molten iron is run off at the bottom of the furnace.

Iron ore + l............... + c...............

waste gases

carbon burns here

blasts of hot air

m...............

The blast furnace

Guided **(a)** Complete the labels on the diagram.

(3 marks)

(b) Write a word equation for the overall reduction reaction between iron oxide and carbon.

.... *(2 marks)*

> When writing word equations, only use the proper chemical names and ignore other information.

(c) Explain why the cast iron formed in the blast furnace has limited uses.

....

.... *(2 marks)*

Transition metals

D-C **1** Transition metals like copper have many useful properties, which makes them suitable for a variety of uses.

> Remember, transition metals are the central group of metals in the Periodic Table (see page 112).

(a) Give the names of **two** other transition metals.

.... *(1 mark)*

 (b) State a property of copper metal that makes it suitable for the following uses.

Use of copper	Useful property
water pipes	*does not react with water*
electrical cables	
cooking pots and pans	

(3 marks)

B-A* **2** Aluminium and iron are two of the most abundant and widely used metals. Aluminium and its alloys are used to make electrical cables, cooking foil and in the aircraft industry. Iron and steel are used in the structure of motorcars, buildings and bridges.

(a) Give **two** reasons why aluminium is a better choice than iron for making aeroplanes.

.... *(2 marks)*

(b) The properties of aluminium would make it useful for motorcar bodies. Suggest **one** reason why steel is used rather than aluminium.

.... *(1 mark)*

EXAM ALERT **(c)** The table below gives information about four different aluminium alloys.

Aluminium alloy	Density in g/cm³	Melting point in °C	Corrosion resistance
alalumin	6.9	1200	poor
betalumin	0.87	700	fairly good
croalumin	0.92	980	good
dasalumin	1.04	102	good

> Take care to *use* information given in the question, rather than just repeating it.

> Students have struggled with questions like this in recent exams – **be prepared!**

A student suggested that croalumin was the best choice of alloy for making aircraft bodies and wings. Explain why the student chose croalumin over the other three alloys.

....

....

.... *(3 marks)*

B-A* **3** Use your knowledge and understanding to evaluate the use of wood compared with iron for a footbridge across a small river in a remote country area.

....

....

....

....

.... *(4 marks)*

Hydrocarbons

1 The diagram shows the arrangement of atoms and molecules in different substances.

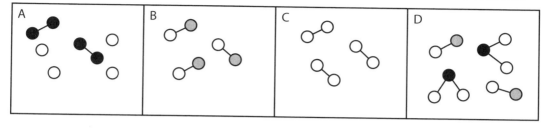

Tick (✓) the correct description in the table below to describe the substances in each of the four structures.

Structure	Pure	Mixture	Element or elements	Compound or compounds
A		✓	✓	
B	✓			✓
C				
D				

> Some have been done for you as part of the guidance.

(4 marks)

2 Crude oil is a complex mixture of compounds called **hydrocarbons**. It is a source of many fossil fuels.

(a) State the meaning of the two terms in **bold** in the above sentence.

....

.... *(2 marks)*

(b) The table gives information about hydrocarbons called alkanes.

Alkanes	Formula	Boiling point in °C
	CH_4	−162
ethane	C_2H_6	−89
propane		
butane	C_4H_{10}	0
pentane	C_5H_{12}	+36

> Take care when writing the formulae for alkanes.

> Students have struggled with questions like this in recent exams – **be prepared!**

(i) Give the name for the alkane with the formula CH_4 .... *(1 mark)*

(ii) Estimate the boiling point of propane ....°C *(1 mark)*

(iii) Give the formula for the alkane called propane .... *(1 mark)*

(c) Complete the structure of butane shown below.

C — C — C — C

(1 mark)

Crude oil and alkanes

D-C 1 The first process in oil refining separates the crude oil into fractions.

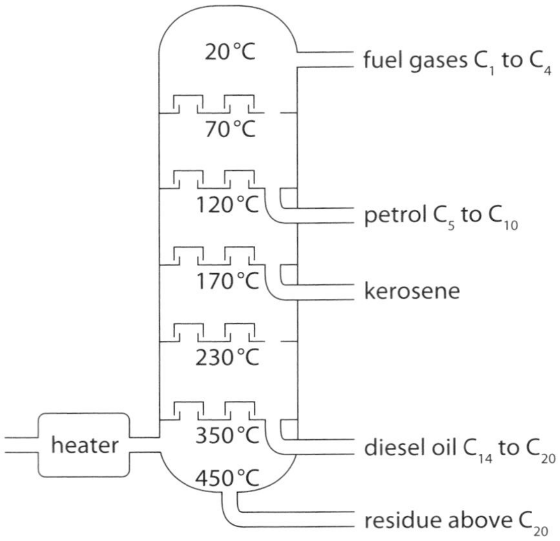

(a) Suggest a range of molecular sizes for kerosene.

.... *(1 mark)*

(b) (i) Which fraction has the highest boiling point?

.... *(1 mark)*

(ii) Which fraction is the most flammable?

.... *(1 mark)*

(iii) Which fraction will contain the molecules shown below?

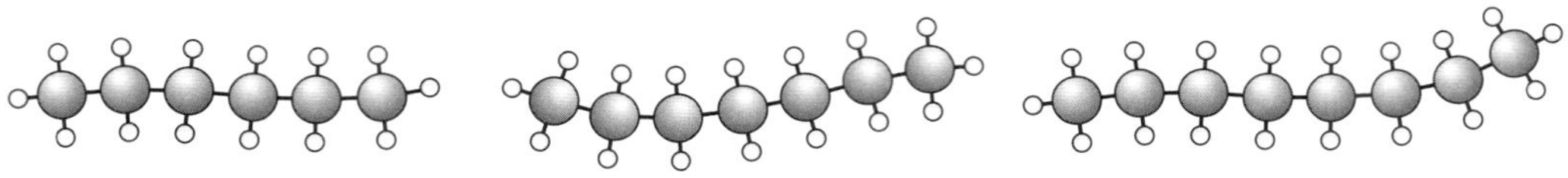

.... *(1 mark)*

Fractionating column temperatures:
- 20°C — fuel gases C_1 to C_4
- 70°C
- 120°C — petrol C_5 to C_{10}
- 170°C — kerosene
- 230°C
- 350°C — diesel oil C_{14} to C_{20}
- 450°C — residue above C_{20}

heater

| Count the carbon atoms in the structures. |

B-A* 2 Fractional distillation produces fractions with different properties and uses. Each fraction contains similar-sized hydrocarbon molecules.

> Guided

(a) Describe the changes that occur during fractional distillation.

The crude oil is heated until most of it has .... It then passes into a

.... As the mixture ....

the gases .... and condense .... *(4 marks)*

(b) The table gives information about some of the fractions.

(i) Which **two** fractions contain butane?

.... *(1 mark)*

(ii) Which of the fractions has the highest viscosity?

Fraction	Boiling point in °C	Number of carbon atoms per molecule
A	less than 25	C_1 to C_4
B	20 to 150	C_4 to C_{10}
C	120 to 200	C_9 to C_{15}
D	180 to 240	C_{14} to C_{24}
E	220 to 300	C_{18} to C_{42}

.... *(1 mark)*

B-A* 3 The liquid fuel used in motor car engines needs to have a low viscosity and a high flammability. Suggest **two** reasons why these properties are important for the fuel in a car engine.

....

....

.... *(2 marks)*

Combustion

1 Many camping stoves use ethanol (C_2H_5OH) as their fuel. A student set up the following apparatus to investigate the products of combustion of ethanol.

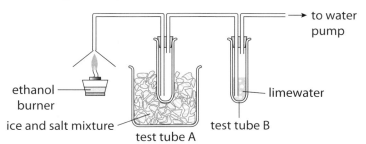

> When asked to describe observations, write about the changes that will be seen to occur. You are not being asked to name the substances formed.

Guided

(a) Describe what the student would observe happening in test tube A and test tube B when the ethanol had been burning for a few seconds.

In test tube A, a colourless ....

In test tube B, the limewater .... *(2 marks)*

(b) Write a word equation for the complete combustion of ethanol.

.... *(2 marks)*

B-A* **2** Burning fuels that contain carbon can produce carbon dioxide, carbon monoxide and soot (carbon).

(a) Which of these products are **not** formed by complete combustion of the fuel?

.... *(1 mark)*

(b) All three of the products can cause different environmental problems. Describe **one** problem caused by each of the three products.

....

....

.... *(3 marks)*

B-A* **3** The flue gases from a coal-fired power station chimney were analysed. The results are shown in the table below.

(a) Complete the table to describe where each of these gases has come from.

(2 marks)

Flue gas	Abundance in %	Source of gas
nitrogen	66	
carbon dioxide	18	from burning carbon in the fuel
oxygen	10	from air
sulfur dioxide	4	

(b) What is the percentage of other gases that is present in the flue gases?

....

.... *(1 mark)*

(c) Sulfur dioxide is often removed from the flue gases by a chemical process. Explain why this process is necessary.

....

.... *(2 marks)*

Biofuels

D-C **1** We use a number of different fuels for transport, power generation and in our factories and homes. Some of these fuels are listed in the table.

Explain what is meant by each of the following statements about these fuels.

Fuel	Source of fuel
biodiesel	processing of plant oils
coal	deep mining or open cast mining
ethanol	fermentation of sugars from plants
hydrogen	electrolysis of water
petrol	fractional distillation of crude oil

(a) Ethanol and biodiesel are examples of biofuels.

.... *(1 mark)*

(b) Hydrogen is a renewable fuel.

.... *(1 mark)*

Guided

(c) Coal is safer to transport than hydrogen.

Coal is a solid so .... *(1 mark)*

(d) Petrol is a fossil fuel.

.... *(1 mark)*

(e) Using ethanol made from sugar does not affect the levels of carbon dioxide in our atmosphere as much as burning fossil fuels.

....

....

.... *(3 marks)*

B-A* **2** Hydrogen can be produced for use as a fuel by using electricity.

(a) Why can hydrogen be considered a pollution free fuel?

.... *(1 mark)*

(b) Explain why most of the hydrogen produced using electricity from the National Grid is not really pollution free.

....

.... *(2 marks)*

B-A* **3** This question is about comparing alternative fuels. In each case suggest **one** advantage and **one** disadvantage of using the alternative fuel named in each statement.

(a) Using biodiesel as an alternative to diesel fuel in motorcars.

....

.... *(2 marks)*

(b) Using coal as an alternative to diesel for use in trains.

....

.... *(2 marks)*

(c) Using hydrogen as an alternative to petrol in motorcars.

....

.... *(2 marks)*

Chemistry six mark question 2

Research into the use of biofuels, as an alternative to fossil fuels, has increased greatly in the last 10 years. The main reason for the interest in alternative fuels is the finite nature of all fossil fuels and the increasing price of oil. However, there are many complex issues involved.

Use your knowledge and understanding of the chemistry of fuels to compare the advantages and disadvantages of ethanol and petrol. Your answer should include references to some of the economic, ethical and environmental issues involved.

> You will be more successful in six mark questions if you plan your answer before you start writing. This question asks you to compare alternative fuels.
>
> You need to compare the advantages and disadvantages of both fuels. Possible issues include:
> - costs
> - safety
> - pollution
> - land use
> - availability
> - storage
> - energy content
> - renewability.

....

....

....

....

....

....

....

....

....

....

....

....

....

....

....

....

....

....

....

....

....

....

....

....

(6 marks)

Cracking and alkenes

D-C 1 An incomplete chemical equation for the cracking of a hydrocarbon is shown below.

> To complete the cracking equation make sure the total number of carbon and hydrogen atoms are the same on each side of the equation.

$$C_6H_{14} \rightarrow C_4H_{10} + \text{.........................}$$

(a) Complete the balanced chemical equation for this cracking reaction. *(1 mark)*

(b) C_6H_{14} and C_4H_{10} belong to the same hydrocarbon series. Write the general formula for this series. .... *(1 mark)*

(c) The missing compound from the equation is an example of an unsaturated hydrocarbon.

(i) What is the name of this series of unsaturated hydrocarbons? .... *(1 mark)*

⟩Guided⟩ **(ii)** Describe the chemical test to show that this hydrocarbon is unsaturated.

Add bromine water; if an unsaturated hydrocarbon is present ....

.... *(2 marks)*

D-C 2 The table below shows some examples of hydrocarbons that could be found in products from crude oil.

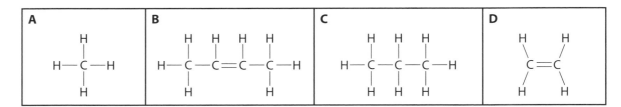

(a) The two hydrocarbons that are unsaturated are .... and .... *(1 mark)*

(b) The chemical name for compound A is methane. State the chemical names for compounds C and D.

.... *(2 marks)*

B-A* 3 Fractional distillation separates crude oil into fractions of similar hydrocarbons. The table below compares the fractions obtained from crude oil from three different sources.

Fraction	Crude oil A content in %	Crude oil B content in %	Crude oil C content in %
fuel gases	6	4	9
petrol and naphtha	10	6	19
diesel and kerosene	15	10	18
fuel oil	17	20	21
bitumen and residue	52	59	32

(a) Explain which of the crude oils would have the highest viscosity.

....

.... *(2 marks)*

(b) Explain the effect that cracking would have on the percentage content of the fractions obtained from the crude oils.

....

.... *(2 marks)*

Making polymers

  1   Most polymers are made from molecules obtained by the refining of crude oil.

(a) The diagram below shows the formation of one particular polymer. Write the names of the reactants and product in this reaction.

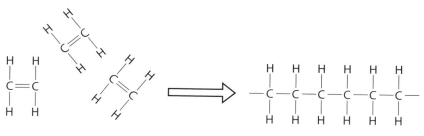

....   *(2 marks)*

Guided **(b)** Describe what polymers are and how they are formed.

Polymers are long .... made by ....

many ....

(2 marks)

(c) The polymer poly(chloroethene) is used to make water pipes and guttering. Suggest **two** properties of poly(chloroethene) that make it useful for making these.

....

....   *(2 marks)*

> Properties could be: flexible or rigid, strong or weak, rot-proof or biodegradable, etc.

B-A* 2   The diagram on the right shows part of a poly(propene) molecule.

(a) Draw a diagram of a propene molecule.

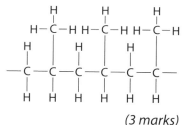

(3 marks)

(b) How many propene molecules are joined together in the above diagram?

....   *(1 mark)*

B-A* 3   New polymers with different properties and uses are continually being developed by scientists. Suggest a possible use for each of the following new polymers and briefly explain why it would be suitable.

(a) Shape memory polymers that are strong and reasonably rigid, but can be made to return to their original shape when warmed.

....

....   *(2 marks)*

(b) A new polymer coating for fabric that allows water vapour to pass through it but does not allow liquid water to pass through it.

....

....   *(2 marks)*

Polymer problems

1 A biodegradable plastic called Biopol was developed in the 1980s for use as a packaging material. However, due to a number of factors, it was not a commercial success.

Guided

(a) Describe the main advantage of using Biopol for drinks containers.

When thrown away, Biopol would eventually rot away ....

.... *(2 marks)*

(b) Suggest a possible problem with using a biodegradable polymer for drinks bottles.

....

.... *(1 mark)*

2 Councils are trying to recycle more polymers. Describe **three** advantages of recycling plastics in terms of:

AQA SKILL
Describe
Page 115

the economy: ....

....

our environment: ....

....

the use of resources: ....

....

(3 marks)

3 Crude oil fractions can be used as fuels and to make different petrochemicals such as plastics, pharmaceuticals, dyes and paints. The table shows the main uses of the different fractions.

Use	Share of total in %
fuel gases	8
petrol	41
diesel	18
jet fuel	11
fuel oil	8
bitumen tar	3
to make petrochemicals	11

(a) Calculate the total percentage of crude oil that is used as a fuel.

....

....

....

Percentage used as a fuel = ... %   *(2 marks)*

(b) Crude oil is a finite resource and some scientists have estimated that, if we continue to use it at the same rate, it will run out within 30 years. Describe **two** problems that will need to be overcome as a result of our finite supplies of crude oil.

....

....

.... *(2 marks)*

Ethanol

D–C

Guided

1 Ethanol can be made by the reaction between ethene and steam.

   (a) Write a word equation for this reaction.

   .... ethene .... + ... → ....

   (1 mark)

   (b) What is this type of reaction called?   ....   *(1 mark)*

D–C

2 Fermentation can make ethanol from a sugar solution.

   sugar solution ——— limewater

   (a) Describe how this reaction is carried out, naming all starting materials and all products formed.

   ....

   ....

   ....   *(3 marks)*

   (b) Explain if the ethanol formed by this method is renewable or non-renewable.

   ....

   ....   *(2 marks)*

   (c) Name **two** uses for the ethanol produced from sugar.

   ....

   ....   *(2 marks)*

B–A*

3 Ethanol can be made from ethene or from sugar. Compare these methods in terms of their use of natural resources.

   ....

   ....   *(2 marks)*

B–A*

4 Ethanol (C_2H_5OH) can be made by the reaction between ethene and steam. The ethanol can be converted back into ethene by removing water. Complete the word and balanced equation below for the conversion of ethanol to ethene.

   C_2H_5OH → .... + ...

   ethanol → .... + ...   *(2 marks)*

Vegetable oils

D-C **1** A student set up the apparatus below to extract olive oil from fresh olives.

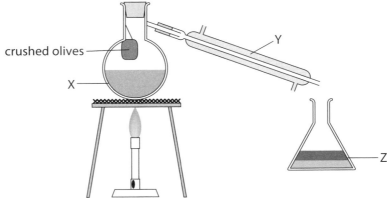

crushed olives

X

Y

Z

> **Guided**

(a) Describe what happens in flask X and apparatus Y during the extraction of olive oil.

In X the water boils to form steam and ....

....

In Y the oil and water vapour mixture is cooled and ....

.... *(4 marks)*

(b) Explain why two layers of liquid are seen in flask Z.

.... *(1 mark)*

(c) Name a piece of apparatus that could be used to separate the two liquids in flask Z.

.... *(1 mark)*

B-A* **2** Vegetable oils like sunflower oil are often used for cooking foods instead of using boiling water. The use of oils in cooking brings certain advantages. However, health professionals are concerned over the generally increasing levels of fat and oil content in our diet.

(a) Compare the use of hot oil and boiling water to cook foods. You should include aspects such as cooking temperatures, cooking times and food energy content in your answer.

....

....

....

.... *(3 marks)*

(b) Describe some of the positive and negative aspects of eating oils and fats, as part of our diet.

....

....

....

.... *(3 marks)*

Emulsions

D-C 1 Mayonnaise is one example of an emulsion that we use as a food.

(a) Give **two** other examples of emulsions.

....

.... *(2 marks)*

(b) Describe **one** benefit and **one** risk of using emulsifiers as additives in processed foods.

....

.... *(2 marks)*

B-A* 2 Mayonnaise is an emulsion made by mixing olive oil, lemon juice and egg yolk. The lemon juice and oil would not normally stay mixed together. However the egg yolk contains special compounds, called emulsifying agents, which keep the oil as droplets spread out in the water.

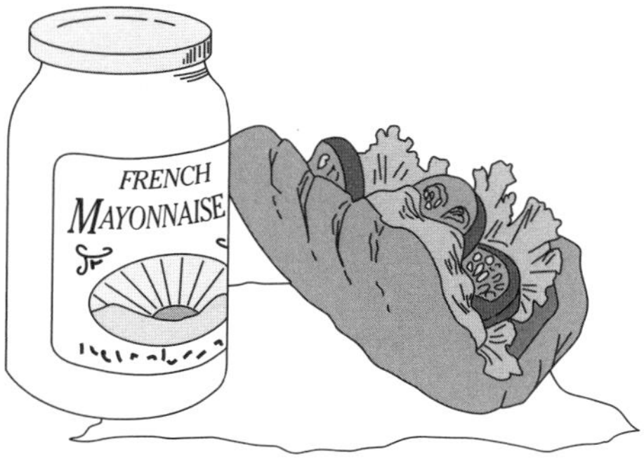

Guided (a) Name the **three** things needed to form any emulsion.

An emulsion is formed by mixing oil and ....

.... *(3 marks)*

(b) The drawing below represents a molecule of an emulsifying agent.

Complete the diagram below, and use it to explain how the properties of emulsifying agent molecules help to keep oil droplets suspended in water.

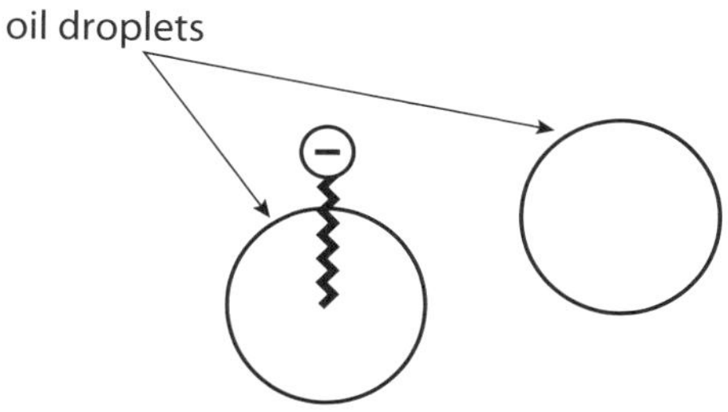

oil droplets

> Use the terms **hydrophobic** and **hydrophilic** in your explanation.

....

....

....

....

.... *(4 marks)*

Hardening plant oils

B-A* 1   Oils and fats contain a mixture of molecules, of different sizes and with different structural features. The differences in molecular structure not only affect the melting points and boiling points of fats and oils. They also affect the way they react in our bodies, when taken as part of our diet.

 (a) Compare fats and oils in terms of molecular structure, physical properties and benefits, and risks to our health as part of our diet.

Fats have higher .... points and at room temperature are usually

.... while oils are ....

Oils contain more .... molecules than fats.

Both oils and fats provide the body with ....

It is thought a diet high in .... can cause health problems.   *(4 marks)*

(b) Describe a test to show the presence of carbon-carbon double bonds in a molecule.

....

....   *(2 marks)*

B-A* 2   Oils and fats are mixtures of **saturated**, **monounsaturated** and **polyunsaturated** molecules. The table below shows some data on the properties of some common oils and fats.

Oil/fat	Energy value in kJ/100g	Melting point in °C	% of different types of oil	
			monounsaturated and polyunsaturated	saturated
margarine	3590	27	76	24
lard	3453	31	58	42
olive oil	3696	−8	86	14
palm oil	3400	35	17	83

Use the data in the table to answer these questions.

(a) How does the molecular structure of the oils and fats affect melting point?

....   *(1 mark)*

(b) What is the link, if any, between the energy value of the oils and their % content of saturated molecules?

....   *(1 mark)*

(c) Suggest a meaning for the molecular structure terms, **monounsaturated** and **polyunsaturated**.

....

....   *(2 marks)*

B-A* 3   All oils can be hardened by adding hydrogen to their molecules.

(a) What commercial product is made from hardened vegetable oils?

....   *(1 mark)*

(b) Describe what happens to the oil molecules when they are hardened.

....

....   *(2 marks)*

The Earth's structure

D-C 1

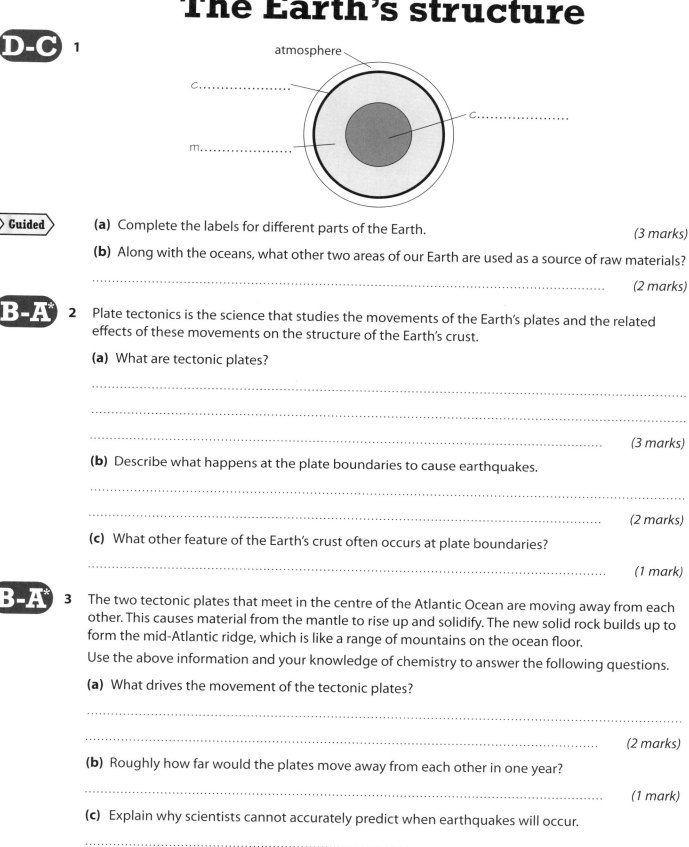

atmosphere

c.....................

c.....................

m.....................

Guided   **(a)** Complete the labels for different parts of the Earth.   *(3 marks)*

(b) Along with the oceans, what other two areas of our Earth are used as a source of raw materials?

.... *(2 marks)*

B-A* 2 Plate tectonics is the science that studies the movements of the Earth's plates and the related effects of these movements on the structure of the Earth's crust.

(a) What are tectonic plates?

....

....

.... *(3 marks)*

(b) Describe what happens at the plate boundaries to cause earthquakes.

....

.... *(2 marks)*

(c) What other feature of the Earth's crust often occurs at plate boundaries?

.... *(1 mark)*

B-A* 3 The two tectonic plates that meet in the centre of the Atlantic Ocean are moving away from each other. This causes material from the mantle to rise up and solidify. The new solid rock builds up to form the mid-Atlantic ridge, which is like a range of mountains on the ocean floor.

Use the above information and your knowledge of chemistry to answer the following questions.

(a) What drives the movement of the tectonic plates?

....

.... *(2 marks)*

(b) Roughly how far would the plates move away from each other in one year?

.... *(1 mark)*

(c) Explain why scientists cannot accurately predict when earthquakes will occur.

....

....

.... *(3 marks)*

Continental drift

1

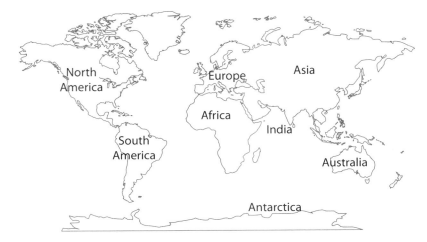

In 1915 the German scientist Alfred Wegener published a book explaining his theory of continental drift. He suggested that all the continents had once been joined together. Then they started moving apart very slowly. At the time many scientists didn't agree. They thought that the position of the continents had been fixed since the Earth formed. However, as more evidence was found, the idea that parts of the Earth's surface could move was eventually accepted.

(a) What evidence for the theory of continental drift can be found in the above map?

....

....

.... *(2 marks)*

> **Guided**

(b) Describe **two** other pieces of evidence that Alfred Wegener used to support his theory of continental drift.

It was shown that rock formations and .... were similar in

....

(2 marks)

B-A* 2 Scientists use theories to explain facts they gain by experiment and observation. A good theory is one that explains lots of facts and always seems to work.

(a) Many scientists did not agree that Wegener's theory of how the continents moved explained how the Earth's features were formed. Suggest how the position of the oceans made some scientists think that the theory of continental drift was incorrect.

....

.... *(2 marks)*

(b) Describe how the idea of continental drift was used to help explain the formation of mountain ranges.

....

.... *(2 marks)*

(c) Describe how scientists who didn't agree with Wegener's theory of continental drift explained the formation of mountains.

....

.... *(2 marks)*

The Earth's atmosphere

1   The proportions of the main gases in our atmosphere have not changed much over the past 200 million years.

   (a) Complete the table showing the percentage of the **two** main gases in the Earth's atmosphere.

Main gas	% in atmosphere
	78

(2 marks)

   (b) The air also contains small amounts of other gases, for example argon, water vapour, carbon dioxide and hydrogen.

   Which of these other gases is a noble gas? .... *(1 mark)*

2   The air is a source of raw materials for the chemical industry.

   (a) Describe how the gases in air can be separated by fractional distillation.

   The gases in air have different boiling points so ....

   .... *(2 marks)*

   (b) The melting points and boiling points of three of the elements in air are shown opposite.

Elements	Melting point in °C	Boiling point in °C
oxygen	−218	−183
nitrogen	−210	−196
argon	−189	−186

   (i) Which of the elements would be a gas at a temperature of −190 °C?

   .... *(1 mark)*

   (ii) Which of the elements would be a liquid at a temperature of −200 °C?

   .... *(1 mark)*

3   A group of students burned some magnesium in air. The volume of air reduced as the magnesium reacted with the oxygen in the air. The students recorded the volumes of air.

   The results of their experiment are shown below.

Starting volume in cm³	Temperature in °C	Final volume in cm³	Temperature in °C
200	20	172	20

   (a) Why is it important that all measurements of gas volumes are made at the same temperature?

   .... *(1 mark)*

   (b) Complete the balanced symbol equation for the reaction of magnesium with oxygen.

   .... Mg + ... → .... MgO   *(2 marks)*

   (c) From the results obtained by the students, calculate the percentage of oxygen in the sample of air.

   ....

   .... *(2 marks)*

   (d) Suggest a possible reason for the percentage of oxygen calculated by this experiment being less than the actual value.

   ....

   .... *(2 marks)*

The early atmosphere and life

D-C 1 The Earth's earliest atmosphere was formed over 4600 million years ago as the Earth cooled down.

(a) What do scientists think produced the gases that made up or our early atmosphere?

.... *(1 mark)*

(b) What happened to form the oceans?

.... *(1 mark)*

D-C 2 In 1953 Stanley Miller and Harold Urey set up an experiment like the one shown to illustrate how molecules essential to life could have been formed millions of years ago.

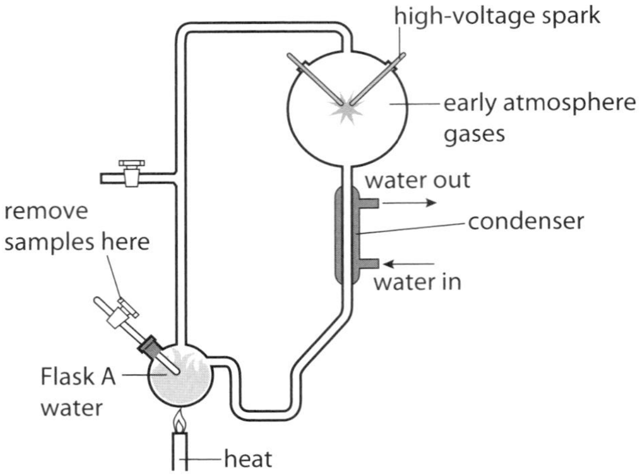

(a) Suggest the names of **three** gases that could have been present in the early atmosphere.

high-voltage spark

early atmosphere gases

water out

condenser

water in

remove samples here

Flask A water

heat

....

....

....

.... *(3 marks)*

(b) What do the following parts of this experiment represent in the early Earth's environment.

(i) The water being heated in flask? .... *(1 mark)*

(ii) The high-voltage spark? .... *(1 mark)*

B-A* 3 Our planet was formed 4600 million years ago. Scientists use data collected today to try and work out what the Earth was like just after it was first formed.

Some information on the atmospheres of other planets is shown below.

Planet	Venus	Mars	Saturn
Atmosphere	97% carbon dioxide 2% sulfuric acid	95% carbon dioxide 3% nitrogen 1.5% argon	88% hydrogen 11% helium

(a) Why do scientists think that information on the atmospheres of other planets might be able to tell us about the early atmosphere on Earth?

....

.... *(2 marks)*

Guided (b) Suggest why scientists think that the Earth's early atmosphere was more similar to the one found on Venus than the one found on Saturn.

The Earth's early atmosphere was produced by ....

which release large amounts of .... gas, the main

gas in the atmosphere of Venus. *(2 marks)*

(c) Suggest **two** reasons why scientists cannot be sure what our early atmosphere was like.

....

.... *(2 marks)*

Evolution of the atmosphere

D–C   **1**   The table below shows the main gases in the Earth's atmosphere today and 3.5 billion years ago.

Earth's atmosphere today	Early Earth's atmosphere (3500 million years ago)
nitrogen 78% oxygen 21% argon 0.9% carbon dioxide 0.04%	carbon dioxide 95.9% nitrogen 3.1% argon 1.2% methane 0.2%

Guided

(a) Compare the composition of gases in the Earth's early atmosphere with the atmosphere today.

Compared to the modern atmosphere the early atmosphere contained no oxygen

....

....

.... *(3 marks)*

(b) Explain why the data on the Earth's atmosphere today will be the most accurate.

....

.... *(2 marks)*

(c) Scientists think that the atmosphere has changed due to the presence of plants and algae on the Earth. Explain how the presence of algae and plants could change the atmosphere.

....

....

.... *(3 marks)*

> Think about the chemical reactions in plants that use gases from the air for life processes.

B–A*   **2**   As the Earth cooled, water vapour in the atmosphere condensed, and the seas and oceans formed. Along with other changes this event had a major effect on the make-up of the atmosphere.

(a) Explain how the cooling of the Earth would lead to a reduction in the level of carbon dioxide gas in the atmosphere.

....

.... *(2 marks)*

(b) When carbon dioxide dissolves in water carbonic acid is formed. Complete the balanced symbol equation for this chemical reaction, including state symbols.

$H_2O(l) +$ .... $\rightarrow H_2CO_3(aq)$ *(1 mark)*

(c) The dissolved carbon dioxide in the seas and oceans can be a problem for marine life. However, some sea creatures need the carbon dioxide for growth.

(i) What do some marine animals make with the dissolved carbon dioxide?

.... *(1 mark)*

(ii) What kind of sedimentary rocks do they eventually form?

.... *(1 mark)*

Carbon dioxide today

 1 Due to human activity the levels of carbon dioxide in our atmosphere have been increasing over the last 100 years.

Guided

(a) Explain why destroying large areas of forest causes increased levels of carbon dioxide in the atmosphere.

During photosynthesis plants take in ....

.... *(2 marks)*

(b) Describe how one other human activity is thought to be responsible for increasing carbon dioxide levels in the atmosphere.

....

.... *(2 marks)*

(c) Describe **two** environmental problems caused by the increased levels of carbon dioxide.

....

.... *(2 marks)*

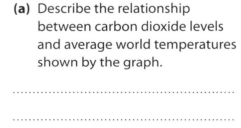 **2** The graph shows the changes in average world temperatures and the carbon dioxide levels over the past few thousand years.

(a) Describe the relationship between carbon dioxide levels and average world temperatures shown by the graph.

....

....

....

....

(2 marks)

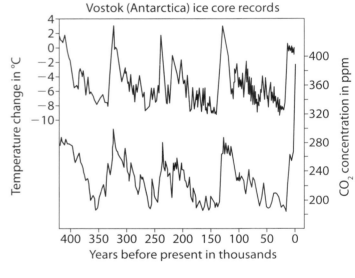

Vostok (Antarctica) ice core records

(b) Why are scientists so worried about the trends these graphs show over recent years?

....

.... *(2 marks)*

 3 The average world temperatures have been increasing in recent years. If this continues it may cause drastic changes to our environment that will affect our way of life.

(a) Define **global warming**.

.... *(1 mark)*

(b) Suggest **two** possible environmental changes that could be brought about by increasing average world temperatures.

....

.... *(2 marks)*

Chemistry six mark question 3

Scientists are concerned by the increased levels of carbon dioxide in our atmosphere and the effects this trend will have on global temperatures and weather patterns.

Use your knowledge and understanding of chemistry to explain some strategies that could be put in place to reduce carbon dioxide levels in our atmosphere. The strategies should include different ideas that could be introduced by **governments** and **local authorities**, or by **groups of people**.

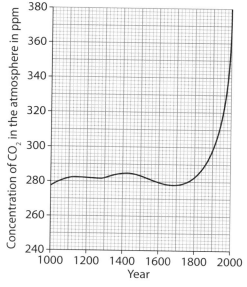

> You will be more successful in six mark questions if you plan your answer before you start writing.
>
> This question asks you to describe and explain. Think of different strategies that would be suitable for each group. Remember to explain how each strategy is linked to an effect.

....

....

....

....

....

....

....

....

....

....

....

....

....

....

....

....

....

....

....

....

(6 marks)

Infrared radiation

 1 A man is going on holiday to Egypt, which is a very hot and sunny country. He has many differently coloured T-shirts. Explain which colour T-shirts he should pack.

....

.... *(2 marks)*

 2 A student leaves two hot cups of tea on a table and measures their temperature every 30 seconds. One tea is in a black cup, and the other is in a white cup.

 Explain which line on the graph is for the black cup.

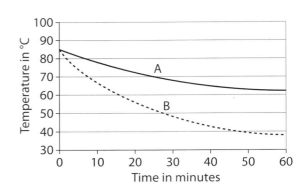

Line .... is for the black cup. Objects with black surfaces will cool down ....

.... *(2 marks)*

> On every page you will find a guided question. Guided questions have part of the answer filled in for you to show you how best to answer them.

 3 A woman's house gets very cold in the winter. She sees two adverts in a local newspaper for room heaters. Both heat up to 60 °C.

EXAM ALERT

(a) Discuss the factors the woman should consider when deciding which heater to buy.

....

....

....

.... *(4 marks)*

> 'Discuss' means to give reasons for or against something. In this case, you should give some reasons for buying both heaters.

> Students have struggled with questions like this in recent exams – **be prepared!**

> The new AQA **'HOT STUFF'** range is great for heating homes. Its features include quick start-up time, safe, hot temperature and a surface area of **1.5 square metres**.
>
> It comes in dull black and costs **£365**.

> The Pearson **'COSY COMFORT'** is just what your cold home needs! The surface area is
>
> **1.2 square metres** and it can be purchased in shiny white.
>
> All for just **£345**

(b) A new version of the 'Cosy Comfort' heater is produced that heats up to 70 °C.

Explain how this will change the heat transferred from the heater to its surroundings.

....

.... *(2 marks)*

Kinetic theory

1 A student carries out an investigation. He uses a heater to heat up and melt a block of ice. He keeps heating the water until it turns into steam. He plots this graph:

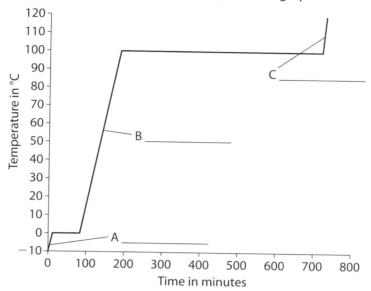

(a) Write the correct state of matter (solid, liquid or gas) next to each label.   *(2 marks)*

(b) Explain what happens to the particles in a solid when they are heated and turn into a liquid.

....

....   *(2 marks)*

2 A class in primary school is looking at materials. Some of the children decide that flour and sand are liquids.

Guided

(a) Suggest why the children might think these materials are liquids.

    Flour and sand can both be poured, and they ....

....   *(2 marks)*

> This part of the question has two marks. This means that you need to include two different ideas in your answer.

(b) Explain, using ideas about particles, why these materials are normally classed as solids.

....

....   *(2 marks)*

(c) The particles in a grain of sand at 0 °C are held together in a fixed arrangement. Sand melts at 1710 °C. Describe how the energy and arrangement of particles in the sand would be different as the sand is heated to 1000 °C and then to 2000 °C.

....

....

....

....

....   *(4 marks)*

Methods of transferring energy

D-C **1** The diagram shows a lava lamp. The 'lava' is made from wax. When the lamp is switched on, blobs of wax rise to the top of the lamp and then sink down again.

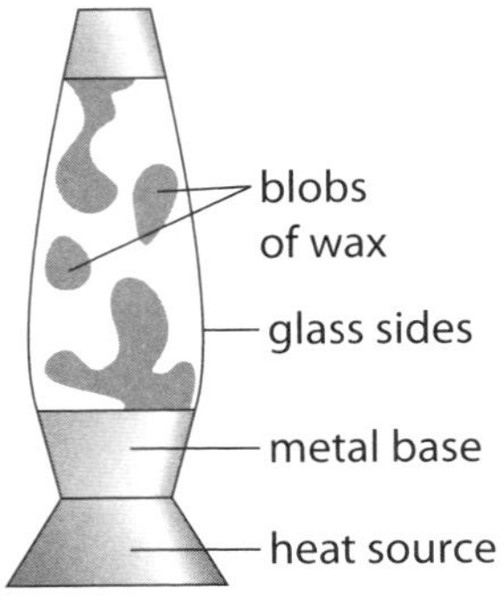

(a) Name the way in which heat energy is transferred by heating from the heater to the wax at the bottom of the lamp.

conduction

(1 mark)

Labels on diagram:
- blobs of wax
- glass sides
- metal base
- heat source

Guided (b) Explain what causes the wax to rise and fall in the lava lamp.

When the wax near the bottom of the lamp is heated, it .... and

becomes .... The wax .... in the lamp. At the top

of the lamp, the wax ....

....

(4 marks)

D-C **2** (a) Explain why solids are better conductors than gases.

Vibrations are passed on from particle to particle, so in a
Solid are very close together so the vibrations can *(2 marks)*
be passed easier than a gases

(b) Explain why metals are better heat conductors than non-metals.

Metals have free electrons which transfere energy
between each other *(2 marks)*

B-A* **3** The 'zeer' was invented in 1995 by Mohammed Bah Abba. It helps to preserve food by keeping it cool. It does not need electricity. The water used to wet the sand does not have to be clean water.

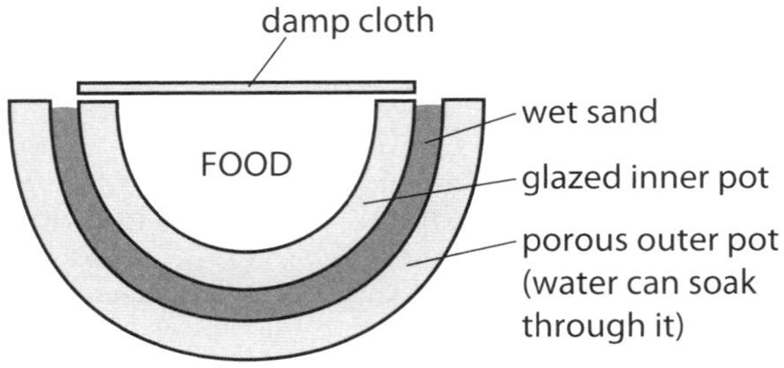

Labels on diagram:
- damp cloth
- FOOD
- wet sand
- glazed inner pot
- porous outer pot (water can soak through it)

(a) Suggest why the inner pot has a waterproof glaze.

It stops the water from the sand contaminating the *(1 mark)*
food

(b) Explain how the zeer keeps food cool.

> You need to use ideas about energy transfer by evaporation in your answer.

....

....

....

(3 marks)

Rate of energy transfer

D-C 1 The diagram below shows the internal structure of a vacuum flask.

(a) Explain how each of the features helps to keep a hot liquid inside the flask hot.

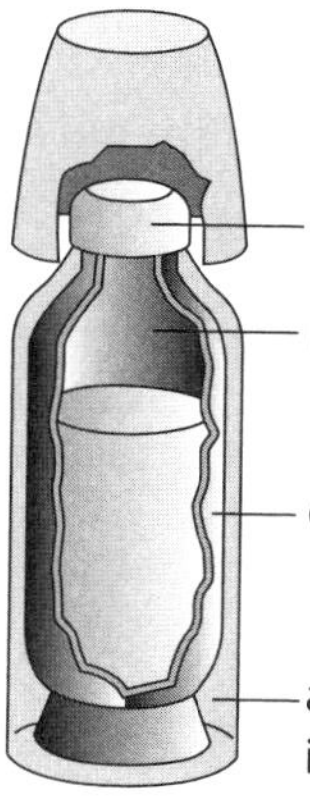

....

....

....

....

....

....

— plastic bung

— inner silver mirror

— outer silver mirror

— air gap between inner and outer skins

(4 marks)

Guided (b) Explain why a vacuum flask can keep hot liquids hot, but can also keep cold liquids cold.

Metals have free ....,

which can .... *(2 marks)*

B-A* 2 Weather forecasters often mention 'wind chill'. This means that on a windy day the temperature outside feels colder than it really is.

(a) Explain what happens to the air around your body when you are outside on a day with no wind.

....

....

.... *(3 marks)*

(b) Explain why you feel colder on a windy day.

....

....

.... *(3 marks)*

B-A* 3 Humidity is a measure of the amount of water vapour in the air. Explain why you feel 'hot and sticky' on a hot, humid day, whereas the same temperature in dry air can feel more comfortable.

> The question is asking about how humans might feel in different weather, so your answer should be about sweating, evaporation and condensation.

....

....

....

....

.... *(4 marks)*

Keeping warm

D-C   **1**   A householder is considering some ways of reducing her energy bills.

Use the information in the table to answer the questions that follow.

Energy saving method	Initial cost	Saving per year	Payback time
double glazing	£6000	£120	
solar PV panels	£14 000	£1400	10 years
loft insulation	£600	£50	12 years
cavity wall insulation	£1200	£60	20 years

(a) Calculate the payback time for double glazing.

....

....

Payback time = ... years   *(2 marks)*

$$\text{payback time} = \frac{\text{cost of improvement}}{\text{money saved each year}}$$

Guided   **(b)**   Use information from the table above to state two reasons why loft insulation is a better investment than cavity wall insulation.

It is cheaper and the payback time ....

....   *(2 marks)*

B-A*   **2**   The householder finds some information about the U-values of different types of window. Use information from the table to help you to answer the following questions.

	Window frame	Gap in mm	Filling	U-value
A	plastic, double-glazed	6	air	3.1
B	plastic, double-glazed	12	air	2.8
C	metal, double-glazed	6	air	3.7
D	metal, double-glazed	12	air	3.4

Her current house has double glazing, but the windows have metal frames and only a 6 mm gap between the panes of glass.

(a) Explain why changing to plastic frames decreases the U-value of the windows.

....

....

....   *(3 marks)*

(b) Which will provide the greatest increase in insulation: changing the frames to plastic frames, or keeping the metal frames but increasing the gap between the panes of glass? Explain your answer.

....

....

....

....

....   *(3 marks)*

Specific heat capacity

D-C **1** Some radiators, called electric storage heaters, contain bricks. The bricks are heated using electricity. This usually happens at night, as electricity is cheaper at night. Energy is transferred to the room during the day.

Guided

Explain why bricks are a suitable material for this type of heater.

Brick has a high .... so can .... *(2 marks)*

D-C **2** A storage heater contains 100 kg of bricks. The specific heat capacity of brick is 900 J/kg °C. During the night, electricity is used to raise the temperature of the bricks from 20 °C to 60 °C. Calculate the amount of energy transferred to the bricks.

> All the equations you need in an exam will be provided on an equation sheet. In this book you can find all the equations on page 114.

....

....

Energy = ... J   *(3 marks)*

B-A* **3** A student is investigating the specific heat capacity of different metals. She uses the apparatus shown below. The metal block has a mass of 1 kg.

She tests a copper block. The heater is switched on for 5 minutes, and transfers 15 000 J of energy to the metal block. The temperature of the metal block rises from 20 °C to 55 °C.

(a) Use these results to calculate the specific heat capacity of copper.

....

....

Specific heat capacity = ... J/kg °C   *(3 marks)*

(b) A textbook states that the specific heat capacity of copper is 390 J/kg °C. Suggest why the value the student obtained was higher than this.

....

....

.... *(2 marks)*

(c) Another student carries out the same investigation, but only heats the block for 2 minutes. Suggest which student is likely to obtain the most accurate result for the specific heat capacity of copper. Explain your answer.

....

....

.... *(2 marks)*

Energy and efficiency

D-C **1** Look at the following Sankey diagram.

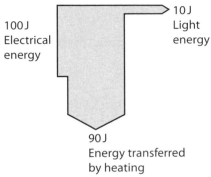

100 J
Electrical
energy

10 J
Light
energy

90 J
Energy transferred
by heating

Calculate the efficiency of the light bulb.

....

Efficiency = ... %　　*(2 marks)*

D-C **2** **(a)** A kettle has an input energy of 1000 J. The output energy is 900 J.
Calculate the amount of energy wasted.

> **Guided**

Wasted energy = 1000 J − ....

= ....

Wasted energy = ... J　　*(1 mark)*

(b) Calculate the efficiency of the kettle.

....

Efficiency = ... %　　*(2 marks)*

B-A* **3** A hairdryer has a power rating of 750 W and an efficiency of 0.9.

(a) Calculate the power wasted by the hairdryer.

....

Power = ... W　　*(2 marks)*

> **Guided**

(b) Draw a labelled Sankey diagram to represent the energy transfer each second in the hairdryer.

(3 marks)

Electric
energy
750 W

> Remember that the size of the
> arrows on Sankey diagrams
> represents the amount of
> energy. Use a ruler to get your
> arrows the correct widths.

(c) Explain how energy transferred by heating in the hairdryer can be useful and wasted.

....

....　*(2 marks)*

Physics six mark question 1

The diagram shows all the features that a building firm includes as standard in their new houses. Explain how the features shown reduce energy transfers from the houses.

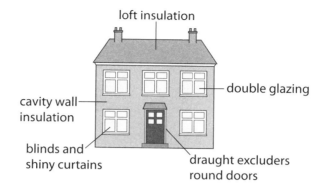

loft insulation

double glazing

cavity wall insulation

blinds and shiny curtains

draught excluders round doors

> You will be more successful in six mark questions if you plan your answer before you start writing.
>
> Think about the physics involved in your answer. Think about how each of the features reduces energy transfers by conduction, convection and radiation.

....

....

....

....

....

....

....

....

....

....

....

....

....

....

....

....

....

....

....

.... *(6 marks)*

Electrical appliances

1 A cook uses a microwave oven for 30 minutes to defrost a chicken. The power rating of the microwave oven is 750 W. One kilowatt-hour (1 kWh) of electrical energy costs 12p. How much will it cost to defrost the chicken?

> Guided

Power in kW = ___0.75___

Cost (in pence) = power (in kW) × time (in hours) × cost per unit (in pence)

Cost (in pence) = ___0.75___ × ~~30mins~~ ___0.5___ × ___12___

Cost (in pence) = ___4.5___ p   *(3 marks)*

2 A restaurant worker boils water in a kettle. The kettle has a power rating of 3000 W and is used for 5 minutes. How much energy is transferred by the kettle? Give your answer in joules.

3000w × 300 ~~sec~~ (5×60) = 900,000

Energy transferred = ___900,000___ J   *(2 marks)*

3 A chef uses an electric oven with a power rating of 2400 W for 45 minutes. How much energy will be transferred? Give your answer in kilowatt-hours.

Energy transferred = _____ kWh   *(3 marks)*

> Make sure you know the difference between watts (W) and kilowatt-hours (kWh).

4 A family's electricity meter readings were taken in March and then three months later in June.

The electricity supplier charges 14p for 1 kilowatt-hour of electricity. What is the family's bill for this period of time?

1 March

2 9 6 3 8
10,000 1,000 100 10 1

1 June

3 0 7 4 5
10,000 1,000 100 10 1

Cost = _____ p   *(2 marks)*

5 It costs £1.60 to use a 2000 W electric fire for 5 hours. Calculate the cost per kWh of the electricity.

Cost per kWh = _____ p   *(2 marks)*

Choosing appliances

D-C   **1**   The information in the table below concerns appliances that all usefully transfer energy by heating. Use the information to answer the questions that follow.

Appliance	Cost of appliance	Power rating	Efficiency	Useful power
sandwich toaster	£30	600 W	64%	600 W × 64% = 384 W
microwave	£56	800 W	95%	800w × 95% = 760 w
electric grill	£40	1400 W	32%	1400w × 32% = 448w
toaster	£18	1000 W	88%	1000w × 88% = 880w

Guided

(a) Fill in the final column to show how much useful power is available to each of the appliances.

(4 marks)

(b) Explain which appliance wastes the smallest fraction of the energy it uses.

Microwave because it has the highest efficiency

(2 marks)

(c) Which device generates the most useful power?

~~Toaster~~ Microwave.

(1 mark)

(d) The toaster is more cost-effective than the electric grill in terms of the energy transferred compared to the cost of the appliance.

(i) Show that this statement is correct.

The toaster is more cost-effective because 880w/18=49w/£ whereas the grill only has 448w/£40 = 11.2w/£

(2 marks)

> You will have to carry out a calculation for the grill and the toaster. Look at the cost of the appliance as well as its efficiency.

(ii) Suggest why someone might still buy the grill instead of the toaster.

You can cook more things with a grill compared to a toaster

(1 mark)

B-A*   **2**   A family lives in a cottage on a remote Scottish island. There is no mains electricity supply, so they use a diesel generator to produce electricity. They are considering buying either a microwave oven or a slow cooker. They have found the following adverts.

Microwave oven 850 W Cooks food much faster than in a normal oven. A whole meal ready in less than half an hour!	**Slow cooker** 200 W Tender meat and juicy casseroles, much better than a microwave and much cheaper than using a normal oven! Put your meal in after breakfast, and it will be ready at dinner time!

Suggest which cooker would be the most suitable for this family. Include calculations as part of your answer.

(3 marks)

Generating electricity

D-C **1** Fill in the missing gaps in the sentences below:

Fossil fuels release energy when they are ....

Examples of fossil fuels include coal, oil and ....

Fossil fuels also release pollutants that can damage the ....

(3 marks)

D-C **2** **(a)** Describe how electricity is generated in a fossil-fuelled power station.

....

....

.... *(3 marks)*

⟩ **Guided** ⟩ **(b)** Explain **one** advantage and **one** disadvantage of nuclear power stations compared with power stations that burn fossil fuels.

Advantage: Nuclear fuels do not release carbon dioxide or ....

This means there is less air pollution.

Disadvantage: ....

.... *(4 marks)*

B-A* **3** The table below gives some information on different sources of energy used in power stations.

Source of energy	% of electricity generated in the UK	Cost in p/kWh	Cost to build in £/kW	Lifetime of power station in years
coal	43	10.5	1800	45
natural gas	41	8.0	700	30
nuclear	15	9.9	3000	60

(AQA SKILL Evaluate Page 115)

A politician looking at the data in the table decides that all new power stations should be gas-fired rather than coal-fired or nuclear power stations.

Use the information in the table and your own knowledge to evaluate the politician's decision.

> You should be able to evaluate different methods of generating electricity, taking into account many different factors such as cost and impact on the environment.

....

....

....

....

....

....

....

.... *(4 marks)*

Renewables

D-C **1** The graph shows how the amount of electrical energy produced by a wind turbine varies with wind speed.

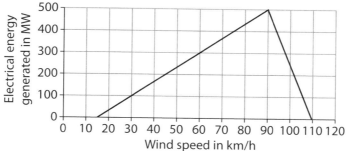

Guided **(a)** Explain the shape of the graph.

The turbine starts to generate electricity when the wind is blowing at about ....

.... As the wind speed increases the turbine generates ....

.... When the wind is blowing at more than ....

.... *(3 marks)*

(b) Explain **one** reason why wind turbines could not be used to generate all the electricity needed in the United Kingdom.

....

.... *(2 marks)*

D-C **2** Solar cells can be used to generate electricity directly from the Sun's radiation. Give **two** disadvantages and **two** advantages of using solar cells compared with burning fossil fuels to generate electricity.

> You should know the advantages and disadvantages of each method of generating electricity.

....

....

....

.... *(4 marks)*

B-A* **3** Most energy companies offer customers 'dual tariff' electricity, where electricity is a little more expensive than normal during the day, but much cheaper at night. This is done because it is difficult to change the amount of electricity produced in power stations, so some of the electricity produced during the night is wasted.

Discuss the use of dual tariffs and pumped storage power stations to try to balance out the supply of electricity during each 24-hour period.

....

....

....

....

....

.... *(4 marks)*

Environment and energy

D-C 1 Compare the advantages and disadvantages of using fossil fuels and hydroelectric energy to generate electricity.

....

....

....

.... *(4 marks)*

> Make sure you give one advantage and one disadvantage for each method of generating electricity.

D-C 2 A proposal has been made to site a wind farm in an area of natural beauty. Give **two** reasons the wind farm might be a good idea and **two** reasons that people might not want it.

> **Guided**

Arguments for building the wind farm: the energy source is .... and it does not

....

Arguments against building the wind farm: the turbines will cause ....

and .... *(4 marks)*

B-A* 3 There are two main reasons why many people support the development of renewable energy resources. Some are concerned about the environmental effects of burning fossil fuels, and some are concerned that our supplies of fossil fuels will not last forever.

Carbon capture and storage (CCS) is being proposed to solve some of the problems connected with the burning of fossil fuels.

(a) Describe what would happen in a power station using CCS.

....

.... *(2 marks)*

(b) Explain which group of people is most likely to be in favour of CCS.

....

....

.... *(3 marks)*

(c) Suggest **two** disadvantages of CCS schemes.

....

.... *(2 marks)*

B-A* 4 Some supporters of biofuels state that the fuels are 'carbon neutral'. A carbon neutral fuel does not add carbon dioxide to the air overall.

(a) Suggest why biofuels could be said to be carbon neutral.

....

.... *(2 marks)*

(b) Explain why most biofuels are not carbon neutral.

....

....

.... *(3 marks)*

Distributing electricity

 1 Explain why electrical energy is distributed by the National Grid along overhead wires at a high voltage.

 Increasing the voltage reduces the .... and this reduces

the .... *(2 marks)*

 2

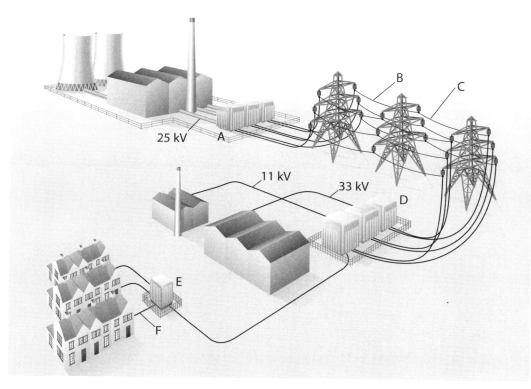

25 kV   A   B   C   11 kV   33 kV   D   E   F

Use words from the box to complete the key for the diagram. You can use each word once, more than once or not at all.

230 kV	**230 V**	**400 kV**	**400 V**	**step-up transformer**
	step-down transformer		**transmission lines**	

A	
B	
C	
D	
E	
F	

(6 marks)

 3 Compare the use of overhead and underground power lines for transmitting electricity.

....

....

....

.... *(3 marks)*

83

Physics six mark question 2

Homes and industries need electricity. As the population of a country increases, more electricity energy needs to be produced. At the moment a lot of electricity in the UK is supplied by coal-fired power stations.

The decision has been made to build a nuclear power station close to a large town, to supply the growing demands of the UK.

Discuss the advantages and disadvantages of building a nuclear power station rather than a coal-fired power station.

> You will be more successful in six mark questions if you plan your answer before you start writing. Points to consider include:
> - What are the advantages and disadvantages of nuclear power stations?
> - What are the advantages and disadvantages of coal-fired power stations?
> - Compare the two types of power station.

....

....

....

....

....

....

....

....

....

....

....

....

....

....

....

....

....

....

....

....

....

.... *(6 marks)*

Properties of waves

D-C   **1**   **(a)** Sketch a transverse wave in the space below. Label the amplitude and the wavelength.

(3 marks)

    (b) A sound wave consists of **compressions** and **rarefactions**. Explain the meanings of the two words in bold.

....

....

.... *(2 marks)*

    (c) Explain why a sound wave is both a longitudinal and a mechanical wave.

....

.... *(2 marks)*

D-C   **2**   In one minute, 12 waves crash onto the shore at Watergate Bay. What is the frequency of the waves in hertz?

Guided   Frequency = number of waves per second

$$= \frac{\text{............ waves}}{60 \text{ seconds}}$$

Frequency = ... Hz   *(2 marks)*

D-C   **3**   A bat uses ultrasound to avoid crashing into nearby objects. The ultrasound has a frequency of 40 000 Hz and a wavelength of 0.0085 m. Calculate the speed of the ultrasound wave.

....

....

....

Speed = ... m/s   *(2 marks)*

> Choose the equation you use from the equations sheet on page 114.

B-A*   **4**   A sound wave travels through an iron pipe. The wavelength of the sound wave is 50 cm and the speed of sound in iron is 5130 m/s. Calculate the frequency of the sound.

....

....

....

Frequency = ... Hz   *(3 marks)*

85

Electromagnetic waves

D-C

1 (a) State **two** things that all electromagnetic waves have in common.

Guided

They all travel at the same *They are both traverse waves and travel at the same speed in a vaccum.* (2 marks)

(b) Give an approximate wavelength for:

(i) gamma rays *10 −15* metres (1 mark)

(ii) radio waves *10,000* metres (1 mark)

(c) Write down two ways (other than wavelength) in which gamma rays are different from radio waves.

Gamma waves have a higher frequency and gamma waves transfer more energy. (2 marks)

D-C

2 Give an example of each of these waves being used for communication:

(a) radio waves *radio + tv broadcast* (1 mark)

(b) infrared *remote controls* (1 mark)

(c) visible light *Photographu and of optical fibres* (1 mark)

(d) microwaves *Mobile phones* (1 mark)

B-A*

3 When mobile phones were first introduced, many people worried that they might cause cancers or have other harmful effects. There have been many studies carried out to investigate the safety of mobile phones, but scientists have not reached a firm conclusion.

AQA SKILL Suggest Page 115

(a) Suggest how such a study could be carried out.

The amount of the waves produced by the phone and lengths to measure how dangerous they could be to humans. (2 marks)

(b) Suggest some reasons why scientists have not reached a definite conclusion about the safety of mobile phones.

....

....

.... (2 marks)

Waves

 1 Diagrams A and B both show a ray of light approaching a surface.

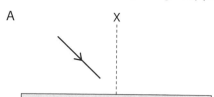   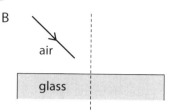

(a) (i) On diagram A, continue drawing the ray of light to show what happens if the light 'bounces off' the surface.

(2 marks)

(ii) What is the name for this process? .... *(1 mark)*

(b) (i) On diagram B, continue drawing the ray of light to show what happens if the light enters the glass.

(1 mark)

(ii) What is the name for this process? .... *(1 mark)*

(c) The line drawn at right angles to the surface is called the normal. Describe what would happen in diagram B if the ray of light was approaching the surface along the normal.

.... *(1 mark)*

 2 The diagram shows a small harbour. The width of the entrance is 15 metres. The dots show mooring buoys that boats are fastened to when they are in the harbour. The waves usually approach the harbour in the direction shown by the arrow.

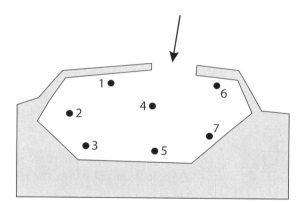

Guided **(a)** Explain which two mooring buoys would definitely be affected by the waves entering the harbour.

Buoys .... would be affected, because waves could come straight

into the harbour. *(2 marks)*

> Remember that if a question asks you to explain something, you need to say why something happens.

(b) Explain which two buoys are **only** likely to be affected when the waves have a wavelength of about 15 metres.

....

....

.... *(3 marks)*

(c) Explain some conditions in which only 5 of the 7 buoys might be affected by waves.

....

....

.... *(3 marks)*

Reflection in mirrors

1 **(a)** Complete the diagram below to show how the image of a candle is formed in a mirror.

Remember that when you see something, light travels to the eye.

mirror

(3 marks)

(b) Circle **two** of the words in the box to describe the image formed in a plane mirror.

diminished	inverted	magnified	real	upright	virtual

(2 marks)

2 Most cars have a 'rear view mirror' mounted at the top of the windscreen. This allows the driver to see what is on the road behind her vehicle without having to twist her head around to look behind. Rear view mirrors are normally plane (flat) mirrors.

(a) The diagram shows a plan view of a driver in a car. Draw a rear view mirror on the diagram and draw rays of light to show how the mirror will allow the driver to see the road behind.

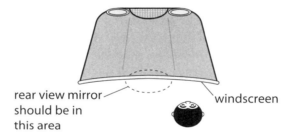

rear view mirror should be in this area

windscreen

(3 marks)

> **Guided**

(b) Some people use the rear view mirror to check their make-up or to see if their hair is tidy. Explain why adjusting the mirror to do this stops it being useful for driving.

The angle of the mirror will only allow the driver to see ....

.... *(1 mark)*

3 The diagram shows a corner reflector often used by small boats. It makes the boat more visible on the radars used by larger ships, by reflecting the radar waves directly back to the ship.

Two mirrors at right angles to each other have a similar effect. Draw **one** ray from each of the sources on the right of the diagram to show how the arrangement of mirrors will always reflect light so that it is travelling in the opposite direction.

(4 marks)

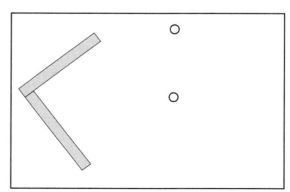

Sound

D-C **1** **(a)** Describe the relationship between the frequency of a sound wave and the pitch of the sound.

....

.... *(1 mark)*

EXAM ALERT **(b)** Describe the relationship between the loudness of a sound and the amplitude of the sound wave.

....

.... *(1 mark)*

> You should know the way that frequency, amplitude, pitch and loudness are related.

> Students have struggled with questions like this in recent exams – **be prepared!**

D-C **2** A boy is standing 340 m away from a cliff. He shouts. Two seconds later he hears the shout again. Explain how this happens.

....

.... *(2 marks)*

B-A* **3** A microphone can detect sound waves. The output from the microphone can be displayed on an oscilloscope screen, such as the one below.

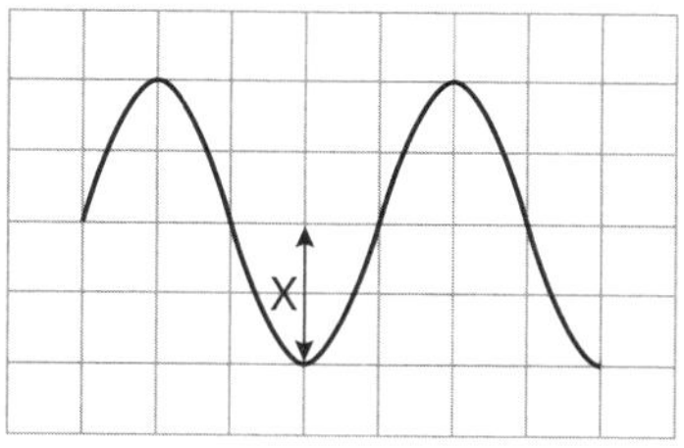

Guided **(a)** Explain what the distance X represents in terms of the real sound wave.

X is the .... of the wave. This represents the maximum

.... of air particles from their original position as the wave passes.

(2 marks)

(b) The same wave is shown below.

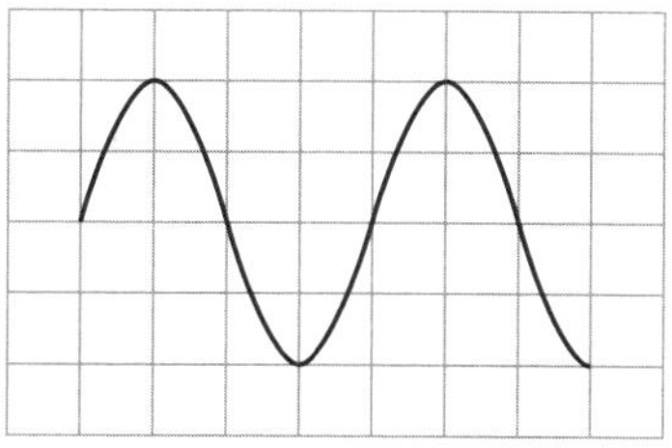

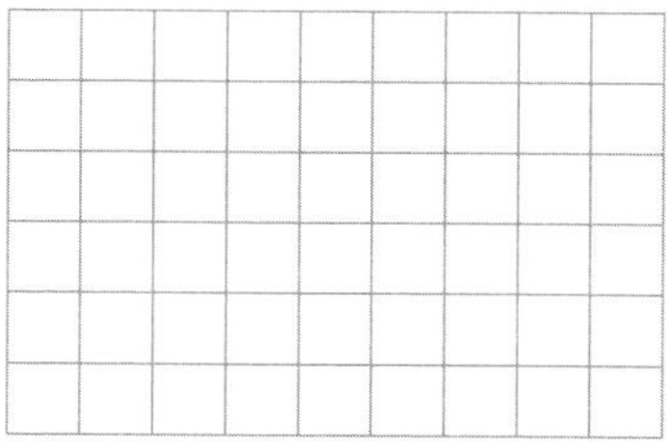

(i) Draw another line to show the oscilloscope trace produced by a quieter sound of the same pitch. *(2 marks)*

(ii) Explain your answer.

....

.... *(1 mark)*

Had a go ☐   Nearly there ☐   Nailed it! ☐

Red-shift

D-C 1 The diagrams below show the waves given off by a siren. Explain the motion of siren A as observed by person A, and explain the motion of siren B as observed by person B.

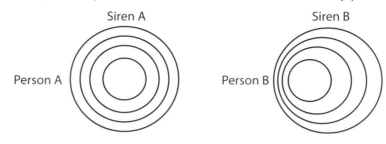

Siren A:

Siren A is a constant wavelength slowly ~~expanding~~ decreasing in wavelengths, the person is ~~the~~ in the center of the sound effect.

Siren B:

~~A~~ Siren B is starting quiet and progressively get louder the closer it gets to Person ~~B~~ B

(4 marks)

D-C 2 Galaxies, like the Milky Way, contain many millions of stars. As the Universe is expanding, these galaxies move away from each other.

The diagrams show the spectrum of light from two different galaxies. The lines in the light from Galaxy X are in the same pattern as the lines in the light from Galaxy Y, but in Galaxy X they are at longer wavelengths.

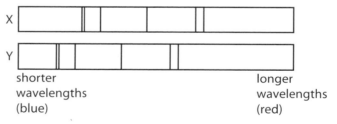

shorter
wavelengths
(blue)

longer
wavelengths
(red)

Guided Explain what this information tells us about the relative distances of these two galaxies from the Earth, and the speed at which they are moving.

Galaxy ___X___ is moving away from the Earth faster than Galaxy ___Y___, because the lines are shifted ___the shifted towards the end of the spectrum___

This means that Galaxy ___Y___ is further away than Galaxy ___X___, because ___the more distant moving away faster.___

(4 marks)

> Red-shift does not just apply to visible light, but to radio, microwave and other electromagnetic waves too.

B-A* 3 Light from a distant star is red. A student says that this shows that the star is moving away from us. Explain why this statement is not necessarily correct.

....

....

(2 marks)

The expanding Universe

D-C 1 The diagram shows four galaxies that can be seen from Earth.

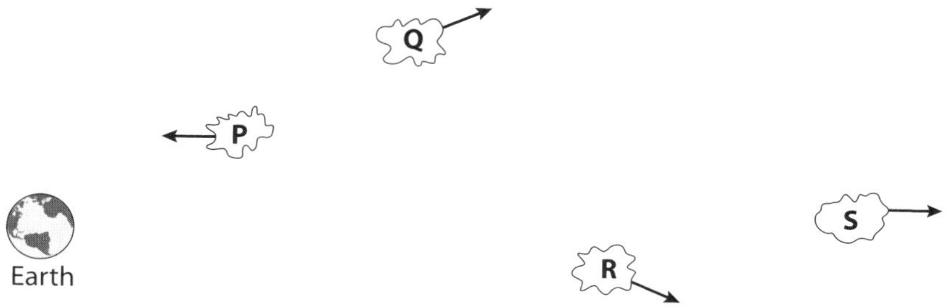

Which of the galaxies is:

(a) Moving the fastest? `S` *(1 mark)*

(b) Has the greatest red-shift? `S` *(1 mark)*

(c) Is not red-shifted? `P` *(1 mark)*

D-C 2 In 1929, Edwin Hubble published a paper explaining the behaviour of galaxies and how they move. He looked at the light that was detected on Earth from a number of distant galaxies and plotted a graph. The graph is shown on the right.

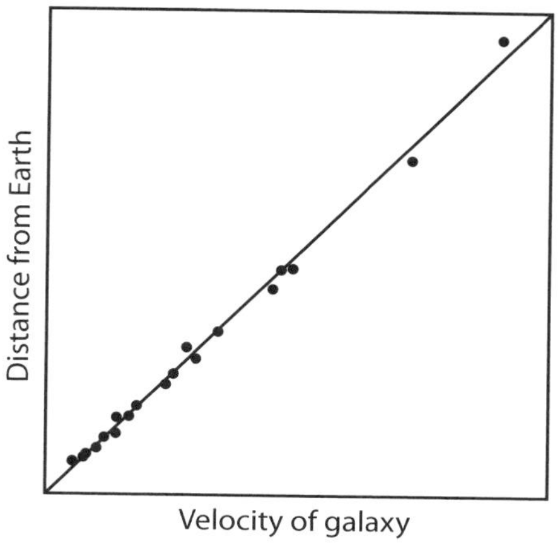

(a) What does Hubble's graph show?

As the distance of a galaxy from Earth increases

The speed of a galaxy increases also *(1 mark)*

(b) What does Hubble's graph suggest about the Universe?

Hubble's graph suggests that the size of the Universe is

~~The speed of a galaxy increases also~~ *The size* *(1 mark)*
universe is increasing.

Distance from Earth / Velocity of galaxy

D-C 3 In 1964, two scientists called Arno Penzias and Robert Wilson found evidence that the Universe had started in an event called the Big Bang, many millions of years ago. They noted that a special type of radiation was present from every direction and that it was extremely weak.

(a) What is the name of the radiation that the two scientists found?

.... *(1 mark)*

(b) How did this discovery support the theory that the Universe started from a very small point?

....
....
.... *(3 marks)*

> You need to be able to relate the evidence of red-shift to the Big Bang theory.

B-A* 4 There have been several different theories to explain how the Universe began.

(a) Why is the Big Bang theory the currently accepted theory?

.... *(1 mark)*

(b) What could happen to make scientists accept a different model for the beginning of the Universe?

.... *(1 mark)*

Physics six mark question 3

Both Infrared radiation and microwaves are parts of the electromagnetic spectrum.

Describe the similarities and differences between microwaves and infrared radiation, and their uses.

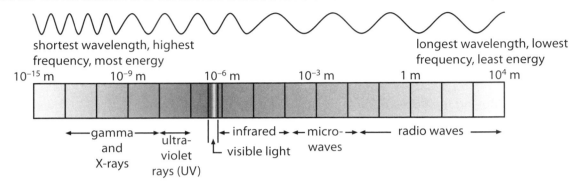

You will be more successful in six mark questions if you plan your answer before you start writing.
Points to consider include:

- What are the properties of microwaves and infrared radiation?
- What properties are similar? What properties are different?
- What uses do they have?

....

....

....

....

....

....

....

....

....

....

....

....

....

....

....

....

....

....

....

(6 marks)

Science A Biology B1 practice paper

Time allowed: 60 minutes

This practice exam paper has been written to help you practise what you have learned and may not be representative of a real exam paper.

1 New medical drugs undergo an extensive series of tests to see if they work and are safe. Complete the following sentences about medical drug tests.

(a) Early tests in the laboratory use .... and animals as models.

(1 mark)

(b) A drug that has been shown to work and be safe in animals is tested on human volunteers

in a .... trial. *(1 mark)*

(c) In a double-blind trial some human subjects are given the new medicine or a

.... which does not contain the medicine. *(1 mark)*

(d) The drug thalidomide was prescribed to relieve ....

.... in pregnant women. Unfortunately it led to ....

.... in babies born to women who had taken it. *(2 marks)*

2 The graph shows oxygen concentration in a stream. At one point pollution in the form of sewage enters the river.

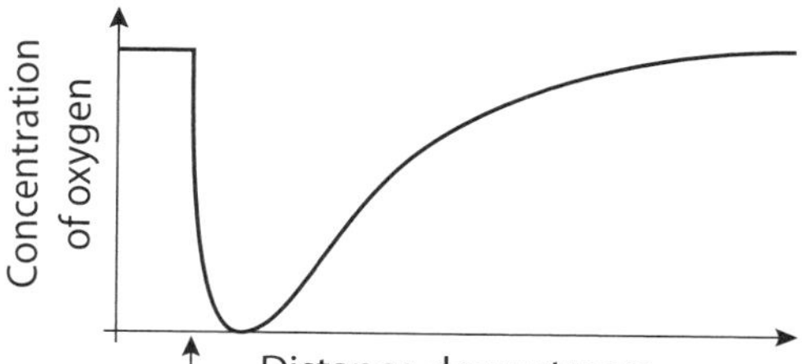

(a) Describe the effect of sewage discharge on the oxygen content of the river.

....

....

(2 marks)

(b) The diagram shows the main animals you are likely to find in streams at various levels of pollution from 1 (least polluted) to 5 (most polluted)

Give **two** examples of organisms that are most likely to be found in the stream just after the sewage enters it.

....

....

....

(2 marks)

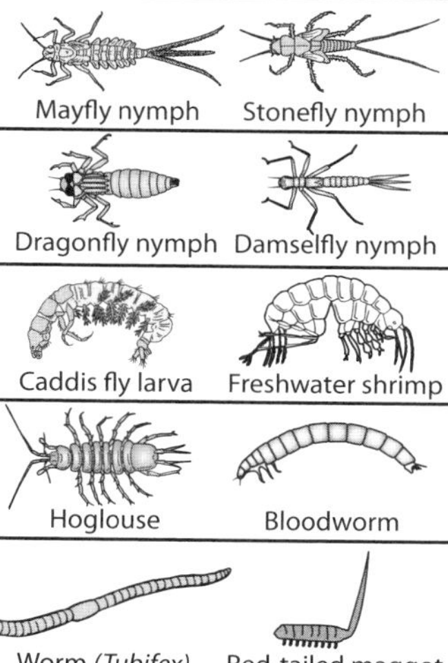

GROUP	ANIMALS		POLLUTION LEVEL
1	**STREAM** Mayfly nymph	Stonefly nymph	If you find these animals in your stream, then there is **LITTLE OR NO POLLUTION**
	POND Dragonfly nymph	Damselfly nymph	If you find these animals in your pond, then there is **LITTLE OR NO POLLUTION**
2	Caddis fly larva	Freshwater shrimp	If you find these animals, but none from Group 1, then there may be **SLIGHT POLLUTION**
3	Hoglouse	Bloodworm	If you find these animals, but none from Groups 1 or 2, then there is probably **MEDIUM POLLUTION**
4	Worm *(Tubifex)*	Red-tailed maggot	If you find these animals, but none from Groups 1,2 or 3, then there is **A LOT OF POLLUTION**
5	No live animals found		If you find no animals at all, then the water is **VERY POLLUTED**

3 White blood cells defend the body against pathogens that have entered it. Describe **two** ways in which they do this.

....

....

....

....

.... *(4 marks)*

4 Uncontaminated cultures of microorganisms are required to do research on antibiotics. To ensure this:

- Petri dishes and culture media must be sterilised before use.
- Inoculating loops used to transfer microorganisms to the media must also be sterilised.
- The lid of the Petri dish should be secured.

In addition, cultures should not be incubated above 25 °C.

(a) State how Petri dishes and inoculating loops are sterilised.

Petri dishes: ....

Inoculating loops: ....

.... *(2 marks)*

(b) State what this sterilisation achieves.

.... *(1 mark)*

(c) State how the lid of the Petri dish is secured.

.... *(1 mark)*

(d) State how the temperature of the culture is kept below 25 °C.

.... *(1 mark)*

(e) State why the temperature of the culture is kept below 25 °C.

.... *(1 mark)*

(f) What does an antibiotic do?

.... *(1 mark)*

5 Drawing A shows a broad bean seedling laid on its side at the beginning of an experiment. The bean has had markings drawn on it at equal intervals on the root and shoot. Drawing B shows the same seedling after a few days.

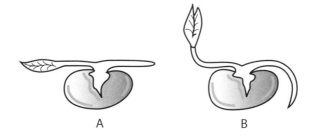

A   B

Explain what has happened between A and B.

....

....

....

....

.... *(4 marks)*

6 *In this question you will be assessed on using good English, organising information clearly and using specialist terms where appropriate.*

The diagram shows the carbon cycle. Some of the processes are labelled with letters.

Describe the processes that occur in the carbon cycle.

....

....

....

....

....

....

....

....

....

....

....

....

....

.... *(6 marks)*

7 A tuna fish is carnivorous, feeding on smaller fish like mackerel. When a tuna eats 1 kg of mackerel it gains about 100 g in mass of new growth.

(a) Give **two** reasons why the tuna gains so little of the mackerel mass.

....

.... *(2 marks)*

(b) The mackerel feed on plankton. In the space below sketch and label a pyramid of biomass for the food chain that starts with plankton and ends with tuna.

(2 marks)

(c) In the food chain, energy and carbon pass from the plant or prey animal to the animal that eats them. Describe what happens to the energy and the carbon.

Energy: ....

....

Carbon: ....

....

(4 marks)

8 Camels are adapted to survive in hot, dry, sandy deserts.

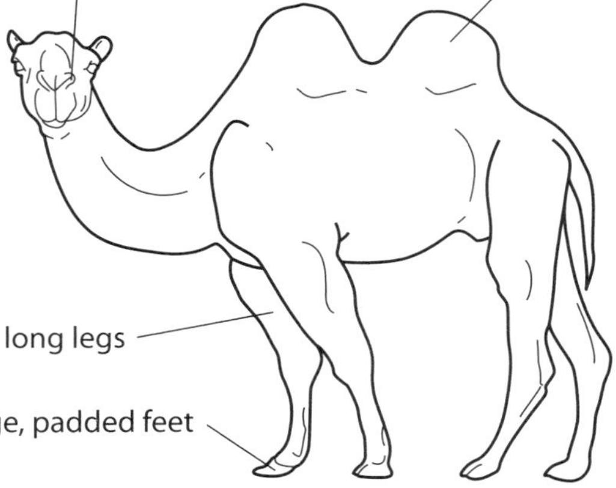

nostrils that can be closed

humps containing fat

long legs

large, padded feet

Using information in the diagram, describe three ways in which the camel is adapted to life in a hot, dry, sandy desert.

....

....

.... *(3 marks)*

9 The drawing shows the way that Lamarck explained the evolution of the long neck in the giraffe.

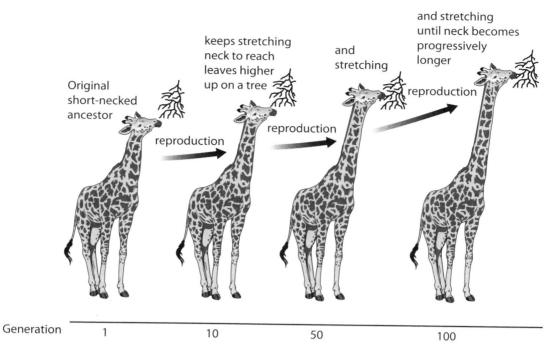

Explain how Darwin would have explained the evolution of the long neck with his 'theory of evolution by natural selection'.

....

....

....

.... *(4 marks)*

10 The diagram shows how the levels of different hormones vary during the menstrual cycle.

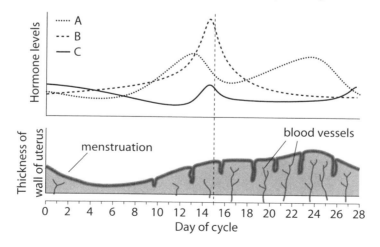

The main hormones are FSH, oestrogen and LH.

(a) Match the three hormones listed above to the three lines on the graph.

A ....

B ....

C ....

(3 marks)

(b) State what each hormone does.

FSH: ....

LH: ....

Oestrogen: ....

(3 marks)

11 A study was carried out to investigate whether drugs called statins lower the risk of heart and circulatory disease. A double-blind trial was carried out using 18 000 people. Half were given statin tablets and half were given placebo tablets.

(a) Explain why a placebo is used in drug trials.

....

.... *(2 marks)*

(b) Explain what a double-blind trial is and why it is used by scientists.

....

.... *(2 marks)*

The results of the study are shown in the graph.

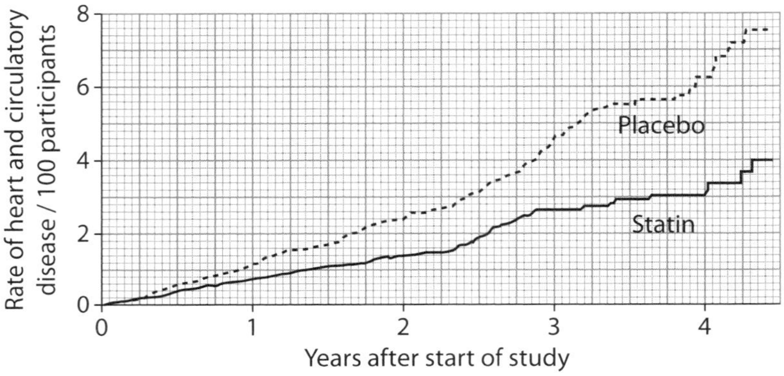

(c) A doctor looking at the results from the study decided that prescribing statins would help her patients cut their risk of heart disease. Evaluate this decision.

....

....

....

.... *(3 marks)*

(d) Explain how reliable the results of this trial are.

....

.... *(2 marks)*

Science A Chemistry C1 practice paper

Time allowed: 60 minutes

This practice exam paper has been written to help you practise what you have learned and may not be representative of a real exam paper.

1 Some light bulbs consisted of a filament of tungsten surrounded by glass. They also contained several other elements and compounds. The thin filament wire glowed white hot when electricity was passed through it. This produced heat and light. Modern light bulbs are more efficient and waste less energy as heat.

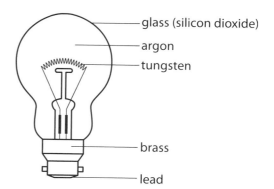

glass (silicon dioxide)
argon
tungsten
brass
lead

(a) Which of the substances in this light bulb is:

   (i) an alloy? ....

   (ii) a transition metal? ....

                                                                    (2 marks)

(b) Complete the information about tungsten and lead atoms in the table below.

Symbol	Atomic number	Mass number	Number of		
			protons	neutrons	electrons
W	74	184			
Pb			82	125	82

                                                                         (2 marks)

(c) These questions are about the gas argon.

   The chemistry data sheet may help you answer these questions.

   (i) Suggest a reason for using argon gas in the light bulb instead of air.

   ....

   ....

   .... *(2 marks)*

   (ii) Name an element that has very similar chemical properties to argon.

   ....

   .... *(1 mark)*

   (iii) Complete the diagram to show the electron structure of an argon atom.

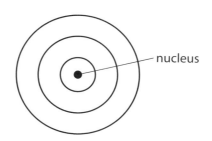

nucleus

                                                                                  (1 mark)

2 The flow chart opposite shows the main stages in producing copper metal from its ore.

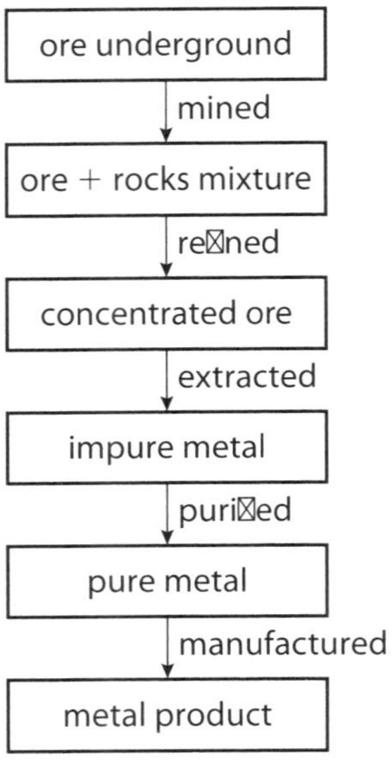

(a) Draw an arrow on the flow chart to show where the copper products would go when they are recycled. *(1 mark)*

(b) Name the process used to purify the impure copper.

....

(1 mark)

(c) New ways of extracting copper from low-grade ores are being researched. Describe how **phytomining** can be used as a source of copper compounds.

....

....

....

(2 marks)

(d) *In this question you will be assessed on using good English, organising information clearly and using specialist terms where appropriate.*

We are recycling more metals each year. Information about the main uses of some important metals and the proportion recycled is shown in the table and bar chart below.

Metal	Use
aluminium	aircraft and drinks cans
copper	electrical cables, water pipes and alloys
lead	car batteries and weights
tin	plating food containers and alloys

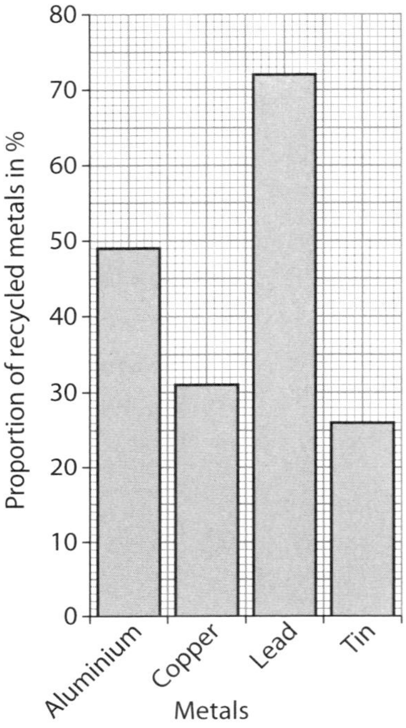

Use the information above and your knowledge and understanding of chemistry to describe the advantages and disadvantages of recycling metals. Your answer should include at least one reference to each of the following issues: social, economic and environmental.

Flow chart (right side):

ore underground
↓ mined
ore + rocks mixture
↓ refined
concentrated ore
↓ extracted
impure metal
↓ purified
pure metal
↓ manufactured
metal product

Bar chart: Proportion of recycled metals in % vs Metals
- Aluminium: 49
- Copper: 31
- Lead: 72
- Tin: 26

....

....

....

....

....

....

....

....

....

....

....

(6 marks)

3 The following chemical equation outlines the photosynthesis reaction that produces glucose in plants.

$6CO_2 + 6H_2O \rightarrow C_6H_{12}O_6 + 6O_2$

(a) Describe this reaction in terms of the names of the substances and the number of molecules involved.

....

.... *(2 marks)*

(b) In some countries the glucose from plants is converted into ethanol, which is used as a replacement for petrol in cars.

Suggest a reason why certain countries use ethanol rather than petrol.

....

.... *(1 mark)*

(c) Petrol is a mixture of hydrocarbon molecules of varying length. Most of these molecules belong to a series of compounds called alkanes. The alkane shown below is called octane and is found in petrol.

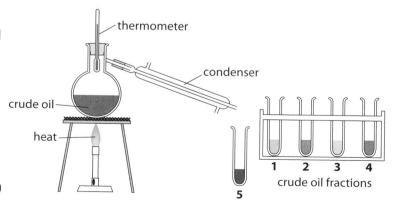

What is the molecular formula of octane? .... *(1 mark)*

(d) Many carbon containing compounds belong to series of compounds which have similar properties. Ethane is a member of the alkane series and ethanol (alcohol) is a member of the alcohol series.

The table below shows information about some of the alkanols. Complete the table below by adding the missing formula and suggesting a value for the missing boiling point.

Alcohol	Formula	Boiling point in °C
methanol	CH_4O	65
ethanol	C_2H_6O	79
propanol		97
butanol	$C_4H_{10}O$	
pentanol	$C_5H_{12}O$	138

(2 marks)

4 A teacher used the apparatus shown below to separate crude oil into fractions. Five fractions were collected and labelled 1 to 5.

(a) Describe what happens in the condenser.

....

....

(1 mark)

thermometer

condenser

crude oil

heat

1   2   3   4
crude oil fractions
5

(b) Fraction 1 was collected first and fraction 5 was collected last.

Which of the fractions 1 to 5 fit the following descriptions?

(i) The fraction with the highest boiling point is .... *(1 mark)*

(ii) The fraction that is most flammable is .... *(1 mark)*

101

(c) The second process in oil refining after fractional distillation usually involves cracking some of the fractions. Explain why cracking hydrocarbons is carried out.

....

.... *(2 marks)*

(d) Complete the equation below, which represents the reaction that breaks up hexane.

$C_6H_{14} \rightarrow C_2H_4 +$ .... *(1 mark)*

(e) The compound with the formula **C_2H_4** is an alkene.

(i) What is the chemical name for this compound? .... *(1 mark)*

(ii) Describe a chemical test which would show the difference between C_2H_6 and C_2H_4.

....

.... *(2 marks)*

(iii) Propene C_3H_6 is another example of an alkene. Suggest a commercial product that could be made from propene.

.... *(1 mark)*

5   The table below shows information about different fuels.

Fuel	Cost per unit of energy in £	How easily lit	Pollution	Renewable or not renewable	Availability	Transport
coal	0.08	difficult	high	not renewable	plentiful	lorries and trains
biodiesel	0.13	fairly easy	medium	renewable	limited	tanker or barrel
hydrogen	0.29	easy	none	either (depending on how the hydrogen is produced)	limited	pressurised tankers
diesel	0.14	easy	medium	not renewable	plentiful	tanker

(a) Use the information above, and your knowledge of chemistry to answer the following questions.

(i) What is the main disadvantage of using biodiesel in a car instead of diesel?

.... *(1 mark)*

(ii) Why does burning hydrogen produce no pollution?

.... *(1 mark)*

(iii) Coal is the cheapest fuel and there are large reserves. However, it is not used widely in the UK today. Suggest an improvement to the technology used by coal burners that would make it a better choice as a domestic fuel.

.... *(1 mark)*

(b) The same plant oil that can be used to make biodiesel can be used as a food.

Plant and animal oils and fats are an essential part of our diet. However, there some health issues associated with these kinds of foods. Describe **two** disadvantages of a diet containing a high proportion of oils and fats.

....

....

.... *(2 marks)*

(c) The first polymers were made from plant material but we now make most of our polymers and plastics from materials obtained from crude oil.

The structural formulae of some molecules are shown right.

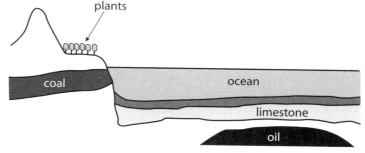

(i) Which **two** of the molecules belong to the same series of hydrocarbons?

.... *(1 mark)*

(ii) Which of the molecules will burn to produce sulfur dioxide?

.... *(1 mark)*

(d) Supermarkets can use plastic bags made from cornstarch, which are biodegradable, or plastic bags made from polythene that do not rot.

Describe **two** advantages and **one** possible disadvantage of using plastic bags that are made from biodegradable cornstarch, compared with plastic bags made from polythene.

....

....

.... *(3 marks)*

6 Our resources come from the land, seas and air around us.

(a) The resources of coal and oil are sometimes uncovered by land movements during earthquakes.

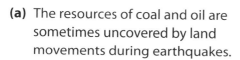

(i) What do areas that experience regular earthquakes have in common?

.... *(1 mark)*

(ii) What causes earthquakes?

.... *(1 mark)*

(b) Limestone, which is found in many places on Earth, has very many uses. Explain how this limestone was formed, millions of years ago, starting from the carbon dioxide in the atmosphere.

....

....

.... *(3 marks)*

(c) When limestone is heated it forms lime and carbon dioxide gas. The word equation for this reaction is shown below.

calcium carbonate → calcium oxide + carbon dioxide

Heating 20 g of calcium carbonate produces 11.2 g of calcium oxide. What mass of carbon dioxide gas would be produced during the reaction?

....

Mass of carbon dioxide = ... g *(2 marks)*

7 In 1915 Alfred Wegener published his theory on 'continental drift'. This stated that millions of years ago the continents were all joined together. They then started moving apart, very slowly, a few centimetres every year. Eventually, after millions of years they were in the positions they are now. However, their movement continues today, at the same slow pace.

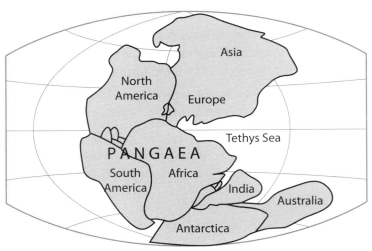

The world before continents moved apart

(a) (i) Describe **two** pieces of evidence that Wegener could have used to support his theory of 'continental drift'.

....

.... *(2 marks)*

(ii) Compare the theory of 'continental drift' and the more modern theory of 'plate tectonics'. Describe one difference and one similarity between the two theories.

....

.... *(2 marks)*

(b) The graph below shows the changes in carbon dioxide level in our atmosphere over the last 50 years.

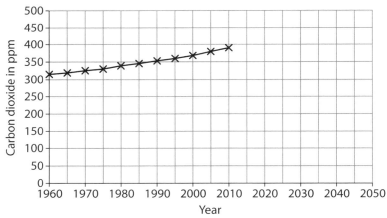

(i) Describe the general trend in carbon dioxide levels over the last 50 years.

.... *(1 mark)*

(ii) Predict the level of carbon dioxide in the atmosphere in the year 2030.

Carbon dioxide level = ... ppm *(1 mark)*

(iii) Name the environmental change that is linked with the trend in CO_2 levels, and explain **two** ways this could affect life on Earth.

....

....

.... *(3 marks)*

Science A Physics P1 practice paper

Time allowed: 60 minutes

This practice exam paper has been written to help you practise what you have learned and may not be representative of a real exam paper.

1 Infrared radiation, light and microwaves are all electromagnetic waves.

(a) The diagram shows the electromagnetic spectrum.

gamma rays	X-rays	ultraviolet	visible light	infrared	microwaves	radio waves

(i) Which **two** types of electromagnetic radiation can be used to cook food?

.... *(1 mark)*

(ii) Which type of electromagnetic radiation is used to send signals down optical fibres?

.... *(1 mark)*

(b) Electromagnetic waves have some properties in common. State **one** of these properties.

....

.... *(1 mark)*

(c) A newspaper reported a scientist as saying:

'Research suggests that the overuse of mobile phones by young people could lead to higher numbers of them developing different types of cancer.'

What has been stated in the newspaper? Draw a ring around the correct answer.

a fact	**a guess**	**a prediction**

Give a reason for your answer.

....

.... *(2 marks)*

(d) The mobile phone research was conducted by interviewing 25 000 people. None of these were young people.

(i) Give **one** advantage of using a sample size of 25 000 people.

.... *(1 mark)*

(ii) Give **one** advantage and **one** disadvantage of not using young people in the research study.

....

....

.... *(2 marks)*

2 Many electrical appliances are used in the home.

(a) The appliances shown below transfer electrical energy to other types of energy.

A 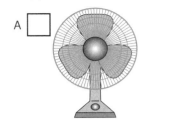 B 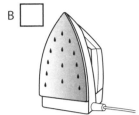 C

Tick (✓) the box of the appliance that does **not** transfer electrical energy to kinetic energy.

(1 mark)

(b) Some statements about electrical appliances are given below.

Tick **three** correct statements.

Statement	Tick (✓)
Electrical appliances transfer all of the input energy into useful output energy.	
When 100 joules of energy is supplied to an appliance, 100 joules of energy is transferred by the appliance.	
An electrical appliance can be 150% efficient.	
Some of the energy transferred by an electrical appliance will always make the surroundings warmer.	
An electrical appliance that converts 500 J of input energy to 380 J of output energy is 76% efficient.	

(2 marks)

3 (a) Diagram A shows a ray of light approaching a glass block. Continue the ray by accurately drawing:

(i) the refracted ray (label this ray 'X') *(2 marks)*

(ii) the reflected ray (label this ray 'Y'). *(2 marks)*

air   glass

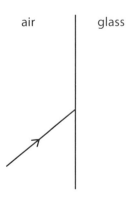

(b) The diagram shows two different water waves passing through a gap between two piers.

(i) What is the name of the effect being observed?

.... *(1 mark)*

(ii) Explain why the waves going through one gap spread out into a semicircle but the waves going through the other gap only spread slightly.

....

....

....

.... *(2 marks)*

4 In the UK, most of our electricity comes from power stations that burn fossil fuels.

(a) Name the three fossil fuels.

.... *(1 mark)*

(b) Step-up transformers are used to increase voltage. Explain why the electricity is transmitted at a higher voltage.

....

....

.... *(2 marks)*

(c) An alternative to power stations that burn fossil fuels are nuclear power stations.

State **two** advantages and **two** disadvantages of using nuclear power stations compared with power stations that burn fossil fuels to produce electricity.

Advantages: ....

....

Disadvantages: ....

....

(4 marks)

(d) The graph below shows the percentage of electricity generated in the UK from renewable resources against the year.

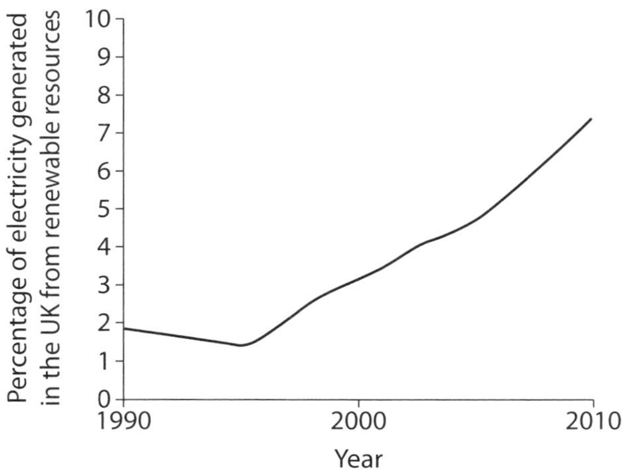

Suggest **two** reasons that may explain the changes that have ocurred.

....

....

.... *(2 marks)*

5 The illustrations show a stove that uses wood as its fuel and an electric heater.

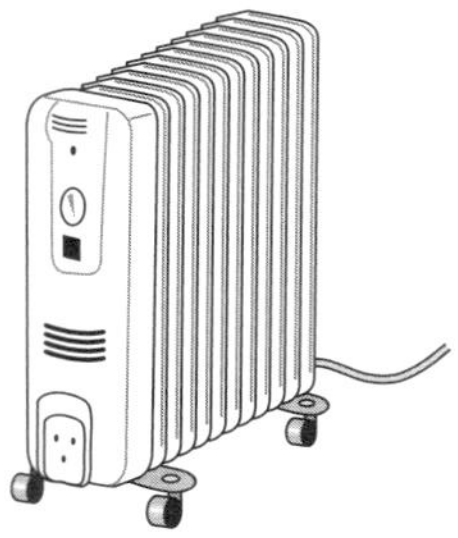

(a) When 15 kg of wood is burned in the stove, 225 MJ of energy is transferred. 200 MJ of this energy is usefully transferred heating the room.

Calculate the efficiency of the stove.

....

....

Efficiency = ...% *(2 marks)*

(b) The stove is used to heat water in a boiler for a central heating system. Below is some data about the boiler:

> **Mass of water in boiler = 75 kg**
> **Starting temperature of water = 10 °C**
> **Specific heat capacity of water = 4200 J/kg °C**

Calculate the final temperature of the water in the boiler if the total energy supplied is 24 MJ. You can assume that no energy is transferred to the surroundings while the water is being heated.

....

....

....

Final temperature = ...°C *(3 marks)*

(c) The electric heater has a power of 800 W and is used for 300 minutes on one day.

(i) Calculate the energy transferred by the heater, in kWh, during this time.

....

Energy transferred = ... kWh *(1 mark)*

(ii) Electricity costs 12p per kWh. Calculate the cost of using the heater.

....

....

Cost = ...p *(2 marks)*

6 The Sankey diagram on the right is for an mp3 player. Each square represents 10 J of energy transferred each second.

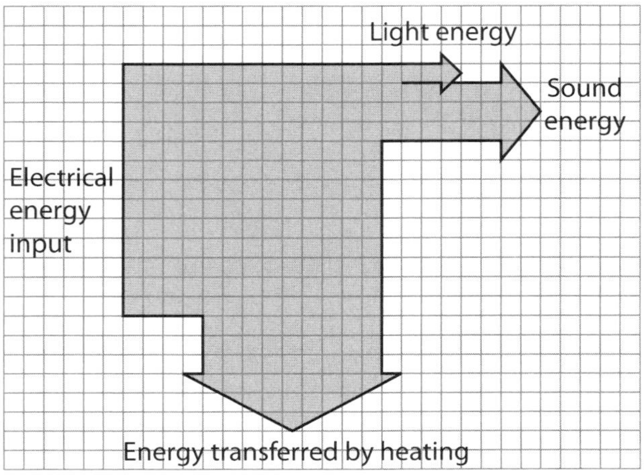

(a) Determine the electrical energy input to the mp3 player each second.

....

....

....

(1 mark)

Light energy

Sound energy

Electrical energy input

Energy transferred by heating

(b) Determine the energy usefully transferred by the mp3 player each second.

.... *(1 mark)*

(c) Calculate the efficiency of the mp3 player.

....

....

Efficiency = ... %   *(2 marks)*

7 **(a)** A radio wave has a wavelength of 1500 m. Calculate the frequency of the radio wave. The speed of light is 300 000 000 m/s.

....

....

Frequency = ... Hz   *(2 marks)*

(b) Describe the differences between radio waves and sound waves.

....

....

.... *(2 marks)*

8 Astronomers are interested in the origins of the universe.

(a) In 1929, Edwin Hubble showed a link between the speed at which a galaxy moves and its distance from Earth. The graph onn the right shows this link.

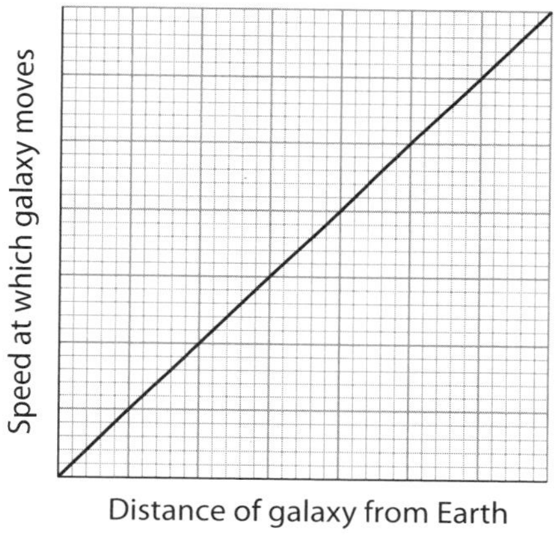

Speed at which galaxy moves

Distance of galaxy from Earth

(i) Use the information in the graph to describe the link between the speed of a galaxy and how far it is from Earth.

....

....

(1 mark)

(ii) The diagrams below show the presence of a dark line in the spectrum from the Sun and in the spectrum from a distant galaxy. This line is always found at a specific wavelength.

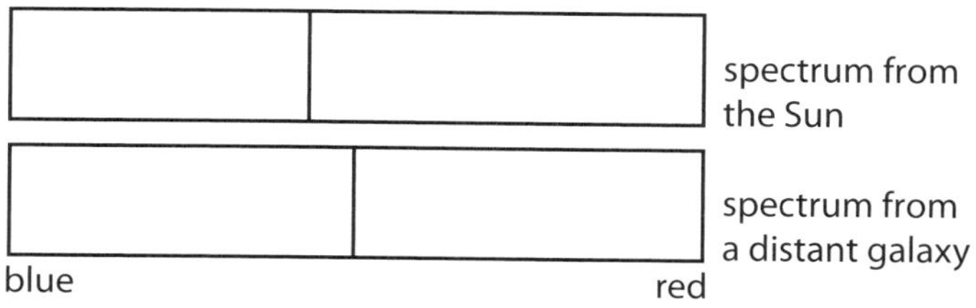

spectrum from the Sun

spectrum from a distant galaxy

blue   red

Explain how the position of this line supports the theory that the Universe began from a single point.

....

....

....

.... *(3 marks)*

109

(b) Explain **one** other piece of evidence that suggests that the Universe started from a single point.

....

....

.... *(2 marks)*

9 The diagram shows a longitudinal wave being produced on a slinky spring.

compression

wall

oscillation   direction of energy transfer

(a) Explain how the longitudinal wave on the spring can be used as a model for a sound wave.

....

....

....

.... *(3 marks)*

(b) The spring is now oscillated more times each second, but without changing the speed.
State what happens to:

(i) the frequency of the wave ....

(1 mark)

(ii) the wavelength of the wave. ....

(1 mark)

10 *In this question you will be assessed on using good English, organising information clearly and using specialist terms where appropriate.*

A homeowner has an old hot water tank that has no insulation. He is thinking about replacing it with a new hot water cylinder that has a thick jacket with reflective coatings inside and outside.

Explain why the new insulated tank keeps the water hot for longer than the existing tank. In your answer, you should refer to the processes of conduction, convection and radiation.

....

....

....

....

....

....

....

....

....

....

....

....

....

....

.... *(6 marks)*

PERIODIC TABLE

Key

relative atomic mass
atomic symbol
name
atomic (proton) number

Example:

1
H
hydrogen
1

Group 1	Group 2											Group 3	Group 4	Group 5	Group 6	Group 7	Group 0
																	4 **He** helium 2
7 **Li** lithium 3	9 **Be** beryllium 4											11 **B** boron 5	12 **C** carbon 6	14 **N** nitrogen 7	16 **O** oxygen 8	19 **F** fluorine 9	20 **Ne** neon 10
23 **Na** sodium 11	24 **Mg** magnesium 12											27 **Al** aluminium 13	28 **Si** silicon 14	31 **P** phosphorus 15	32 **S** sulfur 16	35.5 **Cl** chlorine 17	40 **Ar** argon 18
39 **K** potassium 19	40 **Ca** calcium 20	45 **Sc** scandium 21	48 **Ti** titanium 22	51 **V** vanadium 23	52 **Cr** chromium 24	55 **Mn** manganese 25	56 **Fe** iron 26	59 **Co** cobalt 27	59 **Ni** nickel 28	63.5 **Cu** copper 29	65 **Zn** zinc 30	70 **Ga** gallium 31	73 **Ge** germanium 32	75 **As** arsenic 33	79 **Se** selenium 34	80 **Br** bromine 35	84 **Kr** krypton 36
85 **Rb** rubidium 37	88 **Sr** strontium 38	89 **Y** yttrium 39	91 **Zr** zirconium 40	93 **Nb** niobium 41	96 **Mo** molybdenum 42	99 **Tc** technetium 43	101 **Ru** ruthenium 44	103 **Rh** rhodium 45	106 **Pd** palladium 46	108 **Ag** silver 47	112 **Cd** cadmium 48	115 **In** indium 49	119 **Sn** tin 50	122 **Sb** antimony 51	128 **Te** tellurium 52	127 **I** iodine 53	131 **Xe** xenon 54
133 **Cs** caesium 55	137 **Ba** barium 56	139 **La** lanthanum 57	178 **Hf** hafnium 72	181 **Ta** tantalum 73	184 **W** tungsten 74	186 **Re** rhenium 75	190 **Os** osmium 76	192 **Ir** iridium 77	195 **Pt** platinum 78	197 **Au** gold 79	201 **Hg** mercury 80	204 **Tl** thallium 81	207 **Pb** lead 82	209 **Bi** bismuth 83	210 **Po** polonium 84	211 **At** astatine 85	222 **Rn** radon 86
223 **Fr** francium 87	226 **Ra** radium 88	227 **Ac** actinium 89	261 **Rf** rutherfordium 104	262 **Db** dubnium 105	266 **Sg** seaborgium 106	264 **Bh** bohrium 107	277 **Hs** hassium 108	268 **Mt** meitnerium 109	271 **Ds** darmstadtium 110	272 **Rg** roentgenium 111							

The lanthanides (atomic numbers 58–71) and the actinides (atomic numbers 90–103) have been omitted.

Elements with atomic numbers 112–118 have been reported but not fully authenticated.

Cu and Cl have been not been rounded to the nearest whole number.

Chemistry data sheet

Reactivity series of metals

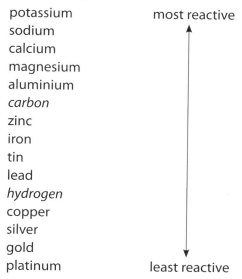

potassium
sodium
calcium
magnesium
aluminium
carbon
zinc
iron
tin
lead
hydrogen
copper
silver
gold
platinum

most reactive

least reactive

Elements in italics, though non-metals, have been included for comparison.

Formulae of some common ions

Positive ions

Name	Formula
hydrogen	H^+
sodium	Na^+
silver	Ag^+
potassium	K^+
lithium	Li^+
ammonium	$NH_4{}^+$
barium	Ba^{2+}
calcium	Ca^{2+}
copper(II)	Cu^{2+}
magnesium	Mg^{2+}
zinc	Zn^{2+}
lead	Pb^{2+}
iron(II)	Fe^{2+}
iron(III)	Fe^{3+}
aluminium	Al^{3+}

Negative ions

Name	Formula
chloride	Cl^-
bromide	Br^-
fluoride	F^-
iodide	I^-
hydroxide	OH^-
nitrate	$NO_3{}^-$
oxide	O^{2-}
sulfide	S^{2-}
sulfate	$SO_4{}^{2-}$
carbonate	$CO_3{}^{2-}$

Physics equations sheet

$E = m \times c \times \theta$	E energy transferred m mass θ temperature change c specific heat capacity
$\text{efficiency} = \dfrac{\text{useful energy out}}{\text{total energy in}} \ (\times\ 100\%)$	
$\text{efficiency} = \dfrac{\text{useful power out}}{\text{total power in}} \ (\times\ 100\%)$	
$E \times P \times t$	E energy transferred P power t time
$v = f \times \lambda$	v speed f frequency λ wavelength

AQA specification skills

In your AQA exam there are certain **skills** that you sometimes need to **apply** when answering a question. Questions often contain a particular **command word** that lets you know this. On this page we explain how to spot a command word and how to apply the required skill.

Note: Watch out for our Skills sticker – this points out the questions that are particularly focussed on applying skills.

Command word	Skill you are being asked to apply
AQA SKILL Analyse Page 115	**Analyse** the data you are given to answer the question. The data might be a table or a graph. Make sure you refer to the data in your answer. For example: 'Y is twice as strong as X.'
AQA SKILL Compare Page 115	**Compare** how two things are similar or different. Make sure you include both of the things you are being asked to compare. For example: 'A is bigger than B, but B is lighter than A.'
AQA SKILL Consider Page 115	You will be given some information and you will be asked to **consider** all the factors that might influence a decision. For example: 'When buying a new fridge the family would need to consider the following things …'
AQA SKILL Describe Page 115	**Describe** a process or why something happens in an accurate way. For example: 'When coal is burned the heat energy is used to turn water into steam. The steam is then used to turn a turbine …'
AQA SKILL Evaluate Page 115	This is the most important one! Many of the skill statements start with **evaluate**. You will be given information and will be expected to use that information plus anything you know from studying the material in the specification to look at evidence and come to a **conclusion**. For example, if you were asked to evaluate which of two slimming programmes was better, then you might comment like this: 'In programme A people lost weight quickly to start with but then put the weight back on by the end of the sixth month. In programme B they did not lose weight so quickly to start with, but the weight loss was slow and steady and no weight was gained back by the end of the year. I therefore think that programme B is most effective.'
AQA SKILL Explain Page 115	State what is happening and **explain** why it is happening. If a question asks you to explain then it is a good idea to try to use the word 'because' in your answer. For example: 'pH 2 is the optimal pH for enzymes in the stomach because the stomach is very acidic.'
AQA SKILL Interpret Page 115	**Interpret** the data given to you on graphs, diagrams or in tables to help answer the question. Sometimes this kind of question also asks you to **draw** or sketch something. For example: 'Look at the data given and sketch a pyramid of biomass.'
AQA SKILL Identify Page 115	You might be asked to **identify** features of something. For example: 'A polar bear has a thick coat. This prevents the loss of heat energy to the cold environment.'
AQA SKILL Suggest Page 115	You will be given some information about an unfamiliar situation and asked to **suggest** an answer to a question. You will not have learned the answer – you need to **apply** your knowledge to that new situation. For example: 'I think that blue is better than green because …' or 'It might be because …'

Answers

You will find some advice next to some of the answers. This is written in italics. It is not part of the mark scheme but just gives you a little more information.

Biology answers

1. A healthy diet

1 (a) bread etc. (1); fruit and veg. (1)
  (b) not getting the correct balance of nutrients from the food (1)
  (c) if a person takes in less energy from the food eaten (1) than is used in the person's body (1)
2 (a) deficiency disease (1)
  (b) Protein is used in the body to release energy (1); and to make new cells (1).
  (c) meat/fish/nuts/any pulse such as lentils or beans/eggs (1)
3 (a) mass of burger needed $= \frac{2500}{300} \times 100\,g$ (1) $= 833\,g$ (1)
  (b) Any three from: this diet is not healthy, as it is not balanced (1); it is very low in carbohydrate (1); and it is high in fat (1); 83.3 g of fat is higher than the daily intake recommended (1).

2. Controlling mass

1 (a) boy C (1)
  (b) Boy A is overweight because he is taking in too much energy from his food/taking in more energy in food than he is using in exercise (1); and Boy B is too thin because he is taking in less energy from the food than he is using/not getting enough energy from his food (1).
2 (a) Group 1 (1)
  (b) People taking the new pill lost more mass than people taking the placebo but less mass than those on the low-calorie diet (1); so the pill has some effect (1), but it is not as effective as controlling food intake (1).
3 Food intake provides us with energy (1); when we exercise, we use this energy (1); by increasing the level of energy we expend more of the energy in our food (1) and convert less of it into stored energy in the form of fat (1).

3. Lifestyle and disease

1 (a) healthy weight (1)
  (b) 68 kg (1) to 82 kg (1) *(In each case, allow yourself 1 kg either side of the answer here.)*
  (c) He needs to eat less/take exercise to lose mass (1) because he is obese (1).
2 (a) the risk of diabetes increases as a person's mass increases (1)
  (b) The total percentage of people with type 2 diabetes is 0.7 + 0.9 + 1.2 + 2.1 = 4.9% (1); so the number of people with diabetes is $\frac{4.9}{100} \times 19.5$ million (1); = 0.96 million/960 000/955 500 (1).
  (c) Those who overeat are more likely to be overweight or obese (1); and therefore appear to be at higher risk of developing diabetes (1).

4. Pathogens and infection

1 (a) $\frac{1712}{47\,938} \times 100\%$ (1); = 3.57% (1)
  (b) Washing hands reduced the number of deaths/reduced the passing of pathogens (1).
  (c) The sample size was very large (1) OR He compared percentages and not just numbers of patients (1).
2 (a) Something that is pathogenic causes disease (1).
  (b) Viruses reproduce rapidly in the body (1); viruses may produce toxins that cause illness (1); and they cause damage to our cells (1).
  (c) bacteria (1) *If you wrote 'fungus' or 'protozoan', this is also correct, although this knowledge is not required by this course.*
  (d) contact through touching with your hands (1); and not washing them, so transferring the microorganism (1). *There are other routes for transferring pathogens that do not appear in the specification, such as: sneezing/coughing (1); carries the pathogen through the air/in droplets (1) OR insects (1); act as a vector from one organism to another (1). You would get credit if you described any of these in an examination.*

5. The immune system

1 (a) An immune person has antibodies to a pathogen and resists infection (1).
  (b) A person gets infected with a pathogen (1); the white blood cells produce antibodies that destroy the pathogen (1); white blood cells learn to make the antibody (1); so that they can destroy the pathogens more quickly if reinfected (1).
  (c) The man would produce antibodies quickly (1) and in large numbers (1). This means that he would not become ill with measles (1).
2 White blood cells engulf the antibodies (1); and destroy the pathogens (1); white blood cells can produce antitoxins (1); which act against the toxins produced by the pathogens (1).
3 (a) Young children are not likely to have immunity to the flu virus (1); as they have not previously been infected (1).
  (b) If those who are most vulnerable to the virus are vaccinated, they become immune (1); this means that they do not act as hosts for an infection (1); so the spread of the disease to healthy people is also reduced (1).

6. Immunisation

1 (a) 2007 (1)
  (b) 6200 − 3400 = 2800 (1); $\frac{2800}{6200} \times 100 = 45.2\%$ decrease (1)
  (c) People stopped being vaccinated against the flu virus (1); or a new strain of the virus emerged (1).
2 (a) dead or inactive forms of the virus (1)
  (b) The vaccine stimulates white blood cells (1). These cells then produce antibodies (1). If a child is infected with pathogens for the diseases mumps, measles or rubella (1), its body can respond strongly/rapidly (1).
3 The virus can mutate (1); to form new strains that are resistant to vaccination (1).

7. Treating diseases

1 (a) The pharmacist's advice would be not to take the penicillin. The man's cold is due to a virus, so the penicillin will not be effective in combating the infection (1).
  (b) Infections such as sore throat are non-serious (1); and using an antibiotic can lead to resistance developing in the bacteria (1).

2 (a) The number of deaths from MRSA went up between 2000 and 2005 (1); and then declined slightly after that (1).

(b) new antibiotics invented (1); to which the MRSA bacteria are not resistant (1) OR improved hygiene in hospitals (1); has helped prevent spread of MRSA (1)

3 Any four from: antibiotics will kill bacteria that are non-resistant (1); but some individual bacteria may be resistant and can survive (1); these bacteria reproduce (1); passing on their resistance to their offspring (1); leading to an increase in the population of resistant bacteria (1).

8. Cultures

1 (a) Any two from: discs are the same size (1); strength of antibiotic solution is the same/same amount of antibiotic used (1); discs left on the dish for the same length of time (1).

(b) Disc 3 (1); it has the largest area of clearance around it (1).

2 (a) This will kill any microorganisms (1); that are unwanted/not part of the experiment/likely to contaminate the Petri dish (1).

(b) This sterilises the loop (1); to prevent unwanted microorganisms getting cultured (1).

(c) This stops other microorganisms getting in (1); and contaminating the culture (1).

3 Any three from: heating the jelly to 80 °C kills any bacteria or other microorganisms in the jelly (1); cooling to 5 °C reduces the risk of harmful bacteria being present in the culture (1); warming to a higher temperature produces a more rapid growth (1); using sterilised petri dishes prevents potentially harmful bacteria contaminating the bacterial culture (1).

9. Biology six mark question 1

A basic answer would include a brief explanation of what has happened to either the roots and/or the shoots.

A good answer would have some explanation of what has happened to the roots and the shoots, and this includes the effect of the hormone auxin on cells.

An excellent answer would have a clear, balanced and detailed explanation of what has happened to the roots and the shoots, including the effect of the hormone auxin on cells and how this differs in roots and shoots.

Examples of biology points made in the response:
- observation that bending is due to growth
- statement that auxin is the hormone involved
- idea that auxin causes cells to get longer
- in shoots
- so auxin is unevenly distributed (more at bottom)
- idea that high auxin concentration stimulates cell elongation/growth in shoots
- but inhibits it in roots
- so shoot bends up, root bends down.

10. Receptors

1 (a) light/sight (1)

(b) It has a nucleus (1) and a cell membrane (1) and cytoplasm (1).

2 (a) Receptors in the tongue and in the nose (1) detect the chemicals present in our food (1).

(b) The ear helps us keep our balance (1); because sensors in the ear can detect changes in movement or position (1).

3 (a) mean for boys = (Boy 1 + Boy 2 + Boy 3 + Boy 4) ÷ 4 = (350 + 325 + 335 + 340)/4 (1) = 337.5 ms (1)

(b) It is fast (1).

(c) The difference between the boys' and the girls' average is very small (1); and the number of students taking part in the survey is small/the data has not been repeated (1); not enough data to support the conclusion (1).

11. Responses

1 (a) receptor (1)

(b) (i) synapse (1)

(ii) chemical released that crosses the synapse (1); and triggers an electrical response in the next neurone (1)

(c) The impulse in the motor neurone travels to a muscle in the man's hand (1). This would contract, causing his hand to move away from the electricity source (1).

2 (a) both carry electrical impulses (1)

(b) Sensory neurones carry impulses away from receptors (1); into the central nervous system (1); whereas motor neurones carry impulses away from the central nervous system (1); towards an effector (1).

3 Any four from: stimulus for the goalkeeper is visual/ he sees the player kick the ball (1); (electrical) impulse passes from his eye along neurones to the central nervous system (1); this impulse is fast so he can respond rapidly (1); brain co-ordinates his response (1); impulse is carried through motor neurones to his muscles (1).

12. Controlling internal conditions

1 (a) hormone (1)

(b) cells would no longer get a constant supply of glucose energy (1); so might stop working/work too much (1)

(c) in the blood (1)

2 (a) The body controls the ions lost when urine is excreted (1). This function is controlled by the kidneys (1).

(b) Sweat evaporates from the skin (1); which helps to lower the body's temperature (1); and keep it at the optimum temperature for enzyme activity (1).

3 (a) breathing (1); takes place in the lungs (1)

(b) urine/faeces (1); this mechanism is designed to lose excess water (1); whereas the other processes will lose a fairly constant amount of water (1). *Note that the amount of water lost through sweating can vary a great deal – but usually only if we have an infection or experience wide variations in temperature – hopefully these won't happen in a 'typical week'!*

13. The menstrual cycle

1 (a) release of the egg/ovulation (1)

(b) The first is causing eggs to mature (1) and the second is to stimulate the production of hormones/ oestrogen (1).

2 (a) The hormones prevent the release of FSH (1); so the eggs do not mature in the ovaries (1).

(b) Women on the pill are 5 times more likely to develop blood clots than those with no risk factor (1); this is a smaller risk than is present in smokers or pregnant women (1); overall level of risk is still very small at only 40 in 100 000 women/pill appears to be relatively safe to use (1).

3 Oestrogen inhibits the production of FSH (1); so eggs do not mature/are not released from the ovaries (1); but high levels of oestrogen led to unpleasant side effects in women (1); so the newer pills replace oestrogen with progesterone (which also inhibits FSH) (1).

14. Increasing fertility

1 (a) using sperm (1); outside the womb/in vitro (1)
   (b) embryo (1)
   (c) More embryos are created than are implanted and the excess embryos are often destroyed (1); people opposed to IVF will see this as the destruction of a potential fetus/human being (1).

2 (a) FSH/follicle stimulating hormone (1); and LH/luteinising hormone (1)
   (b) The hormone FSH causes eggs to mature inside the ovaries (1). The hormone LH causes eggs to be released from the ovaries (1).

3 Any four from the following, but there must be at least one drawback and at least one advantage.
   Drawbacks: the success rate for IVF is still quite low (1); at only 12 400/45 250 $\times$ 100 = 27% (1); cost is quite high (especially if more than one cycle of treatment is needed) (1); total cost to the NHS in 2010 = 45250 $\times$ £2500 = £113 million (1).
   Benefits: it allows couples to have children if they are not able to naturally (1); even though success rate is low, it is still successful for some couples (1); it can be easier to use this procedure than to adopt (1).

15. Plant responses

1 (a) The root will grow downwards (1); because roots grow in the direction of the force of gravity (1).
   (b) (i) auxin (1)
       (ii) accumulates on the lower surface of the root (1); it inhibits elongation of the cells here (1); so the upper surface of the root grows more, making the root bend downward (1)

2 (a) (positive) phototropism (1)
   (b) Any four from: auxin is made in the tip of the shoot (1); so the shoot with the tip removed does not respond to the light (1); the normal shoot grows towards the light (1); as auxin accumulates in the dark side/the side furthest from the light source (1); elongating cells on that side of the shoot (1).

16. Plant hormones

1 Auxin is a plant growth hormone (1); which stimulates the end of the cutting to produce roots (1).

2 (a) +2 (1). *You need the + as well as the 2 to get the mark.*
   (b) The weedkiller is selective, so it only affects some plants (1).
   (c) allowed the same area to be measured out in each experiment (1); so that the data collected allows fair comparisons to be made (1)

3 Yes or no with any four from: the mean result with the weedkiller does show the largest decrease in weed numbers (1); however, we do not know how many weeds were in each quadrat to start with (1); also, the difference between weedkiller and handpicking is very small (1); and influenced by the result for Area 2 of the handpicked, which was a smaller reduction that the other two areas (1); so it is hard to be confident that weedkiller is really the best method (1).

17. New drugs

1 (a) Efficacy measures whether the drug has an effect (1).
   (b) The test is designed to see if the drug is harmful. It is unethical to carry this out on humans/animals (1), so scientists have to find new ways to do this/use tissue cultures (1).

2 (a) pill that does not contain the active drug (1)

   (b) In a double-blind test some patients are given the active drug and others are given a placebo (1); but neither the patients nor the doctors know who has been given which treatment (1); so neither the patient nor the doctor judges the outcome by what they *expect* to happen (1).

3 (a) Large number of subjects make the data valid (1); and repeatable (1) OR side effects will only be seen in small numbers (1) so easier to notice with a large trial group (1) OR there are different stages of the trial (1); and each step needs a different group of people (1).
   (b) Drug appears to be effective in nearly 400 people with high blood pressure (1); this reduction is much greater than those in the placebo group (1).
   You could also say: the drug seems to have very little adverse effect on the blood pressure of those in the 'normal' group (so it is effective).

18. Thalidomide and statins

1 (a) A control group is needed (1) to compare the effects of the drug in the test group (1).
   (b) Both groups had a lower cholesterol level (1); but those taking the drug had a larger loss than those who only changed their diet (1).
   (c) It will lower the risk of developing heart disease/other diseases of the circulatory system (1).

2 (a) Both drugs are more effective than the placebo (1). Drug Y is more effective than drug X, as more people found it effective in treating sleeplessness (1).
   (b) (i) morning sickness (1)
       (ii) This trial was only done on men (1); so was not tested on pregnant women who were using it to treat morning sickness (1); so the side effect that caused birth defects in babies was not noticed at the trial stage (1).

19. Recreational drugs

1 (a) The sample of rats taken was very small (1); and just because something happens in rats, it does not follow that the same effect will be seen in humans (1).
   (b) The drug can change chemical processes in the body (1) so that the body depends on having the drug (1).

2 (a) mental health problems (1)
   (b) People who have used cannabis for many years may find themselves addicted (1). If they try to give up, they may have withdrawal symptoms (1).

3 The data shows that ecstasy and amphetamines are more suited to be in the same class (1) because (any three from): amphetamine causes more deaths than cannabis, but has fewer users (1); cocaine has a much higher proportion of deaths to the number of users (1); and this is much greater than the proportion of deaths to users for the other drugs (1); 27.4 deaths per 100 000 users for cocaine, 5.4 deaths per 100 000 for ecstasy and 8.1 deaths per 100 000 users for amphetamine (1); idea that other factors may also affect the classification (1).

20. Drugs and health

1 (a) Two glasses of wine contain 3 units of alcohol (1); this amount of alcohol increases reaction time by 40 milliseconds (1).
   (b) Any two from: consuming alcohol increases reaction time (1); person who has been drinking will react to road conditions more slowly (1); this could cause accidents as people may not steer/brake in time to avoid collisions (1).

2 **(a)** there has been a general decrease in the percentage of people who smoke (1); but that decrease has slowed down/stopped in the last few years (1).

(b) The percentage of smokers in 2000 was 26% (1). Answers between 25.5% and 27% would be accepted. So the number of smokers was 58 800 000 × 26/100 (1) = 15.3 million people (1). *Note that the answer here is given to 3 sig figs, to match 58.8 million in the data given.*

(c) The number of people who take heroin is about one-tenth of those who smoke (1); smoking leads to a variety of diseases such as cancer or heart disease (1); although heroin is a serious drug, the number of addicts is small (1); so the cost of heroin addiction to the NHS is likely to be less than for the effects of nicotine (1).

21. Drugs in sport

1 **(a)** A stimulant drug increases heart rate (1).

(b) Athletes may take the drug unintentionally (1) because they are treating a medical condition (1) OR it is hard to prove the athlete took the drug to improve performance (1); when it is freely available/has a well-known medical use (1).

2 **(a)** Weightlifter B has a greater improvement in the amount of weight than can be lifted (1); compared with the improvement from training alone, as in weightlifter A (1).

(b) A steroid allows the weightlifter to increase muscle size more quickly (1); so he can train harder/make greater improvements in a short time (1).

(c) Your answer should have a balance of statements in support of the statement (1 mark) and against the statement (1 mark); and a final conclusion (1 mark). Justified: if some people are cheating in this way, then you may also have to do the same to compete on the same basis (1); even if you take steroids, you still need to train hard in order to succeed (1). Against: even if others were doing it, that does not make it right (1); many people look up to athletes as role models and their use of drugs ruins this positive image (1). Your final conclusion should weigh up the positives and negatives and give your opinion (1).

22. Biology six mark question 2

A basic answer would include a brief description of one of the two processes.

A good answer would include a brief description of both processes or a detailed description of one process.

An excellent answer would include a detailed description of both processes with a comparison.

Examples of biology points made in the response:

For embryo transplant:
- artificial insemination of cow
- development of embryos
- removal of embryos from cow
- splitting of embryos
- placing of split embryos into foster mother.

For adult cell cloning:
- the nucleus is removed from an unfertilised egg cell
- the nucleus from an adult body cell, e.g. a skin cell
- is then inserted into the egg cell
- an electric shock is run through the egg cell
- the egg cell begins to divide
- to form embryo cells

- these embryo cells contain the same genetic information as the adult skin cell
- When the embryo has developed into a ball of cells
- it is inserted into the womb of an adult female.

Comparison:
Similarities:
- Both require surrogate/host/foster mother.
- Host mother is not related to offspring in either case.

Differences:
- Embryo transplant gives several offspring, adult cell cloning only one.
- Embryo transplant does not require any stimulus to start division OR embryo transplant division occurs naturally, in adult cell cloning a shock is need to start division.
- Embryo transplants produce several clones of the same embryo, i.e. the offspring are all the same; adult cell cloning produces one offspring, which is a clone of the parent; both require host mothers who do not share genes with the offspring.

23. Competition

1 **(a)** So that they can become the new alpha male (1); and get to mate with more female meerkats (1).

(b) Food can often be scarce in their habitat (1); so large groups need to split into different areas in order to find enough food (1).

2 large, attractive tail feathers (1); peacock competes with other males for mates (1); large showy tails are more attractive to female peahens (1). *You could also suggest that the large tail feathers can be used to help scare away other male peacocks who may compete for females.*

3 **(a)** The trees emerge through the canopy to get light (1). They will also have space to grow (1).

(b) The trees have deep/extensive roots (1) to collect minerals (1).

24. Adaptations

1 **(a)** extremophiles (1)

(b) Bacteria provide food (1); to allow other organisms to survive there (1); whereas the rest of the sea bed cannot sustain life (1).

2 Organism A (*Note that there is no mark for merely identifying the organism!*); any three reasons from: A has thick fur to help with insulation (1); A has dark skin in order to absorb as much energy from the sun as possible (1); A has wide feet in order not to sink through the snow/spread its mass on the ice (1); A has smaller ears so as to preserve heat/not radiate heat (1). *The reverse comments about Organism B would also be acceptable.*

3 **(a)** Roses produce flowers to attract insects (1). These have very bright colours to attract insects (1), and also often have a strong smell (1).

(b) They have a light, feathery structure (1); so can easily be blown away/distributed by the wind (1).

25. Indicators

1 **(a)** The polluted water would have fewer mayfly larvae (first box) (1).

(b) The factory adds pollution to the water in the stream (1). The water now contains less dissolved oxygen, so some organisms cannot survive as well (1).

2 **(a)** spread from the corner of the country to most of England (1); and this spread is very rapid (1)

(b) no, because the spread is going further north, i.e. into cooler areas (1); and the timescale of the spread is too short to be a climate change issue (1)

3 Lichens are sensitive to sulfur dioxide concentration in the air (1); some lichen species tolerate this gas in the atmosphere, while others do not (1); scientists study the change in the pattern of distribution of the different species over time (1).

26. Energy and biomass

1 (a) respiration (1)

(b) Deer use this energy to maintain their body temperature (1); they also need it for their muscles when they move (1).

(c) Any two from: excretion of food that is not fully digested (1); heat energy lost through movement (1); heat energy lost through excretion of warm waste materials e.g. breathing/sweating (1).

2 (a) plants (1); algae (1)

(b) They use sunlight to photosynthesise (1); helping to turn carbon dioxide in the air into carbon compounds (1).

3 (a) mouse: 600×25 g $= 15\,000$ g $= 15$ kg (1); snake: 10×0.5 kg $= 5$ kg (1)

(b) pyramid of biomass with clover on the bottom, mouse in the middle and snake on the top (1); and the size of the layers in the proportion $10:3:1$ (1)

(c) Energy contained in the biomass is transferred to the environment as you go from one stage in the food chain to the next (1); in the form of heat/excretion products (1); so each level in the pyramid is smaller than the one below (1) OR biomass is lost from one stage to the other, as mass is lost from ingested material through faeces (1) and through carbon dioxide lost in respiration (1); so each level in the pyramid is smaller than the one below (1).

27. Decay

1 (a) To make compost, microorganisms that decay the garden waste need aerobic conditions (1), air (or oxygen) and water (1).

(b) Compost contains minerals (1); which can easily be taken up by plants as the compost has decayed the material in it (1).

2 (a) edible waste $= 7.5 \times \dfrac{60}{100}$ (1) $= 4.5$ million tonnes (1)

(b) Any three from: the 'edible waste' fills space in landfill that can be used for non-compostable/non-usable materials (1); number of days of landfill time taken to process this waste $= \dfrac{4\,500\,000}{2500}$ (1) $= 1800$ days (1); this waste can easily be composted/recycled/reduced through better food use (1).

3 The mass of leaves goes down in both experiments (1); decrease in mass is due to decomposition in the leaf/leaf being eaten by organisms in the soil (1); but the loss of mass is greater in the bag with large mesh (1); because they can be more easily eaten by organisms in the soil/the pieces of leaves can fall out when the bag is moved (1).

28. Carbon cycling

1 (a) bacteria/fungus (1)

(b) Decomposers also feed on excreted matter like faeces/manure (1).

(c) This source is fossil fuels/coal/oil/gas (1); and the carbon is returned back to the atmosphere as carbon dioxide (1); during combustion/when the fuel is burned (1).

2 (a) photosynthesis (1)

(b) The algae use carbon dioxide to make carbohydrates/fats/proteins (1); which are used to make up new cells/new biomass/for energy (1).

3 Any four from: only process removing carbon from the atmosphere is photosynthesis (1); this is the source of all the carbon in the plants (1); so only this carbon can be passed back into the atmosphere by respiration, or passed on to animals (1); but not all the plants are eaten/carbon in plants that are eaten converted to carbon compounds in animals (1); therefore this part of the cycle represents no net increase in carbon dioxide in the atmosphere (1).

29. Genes

1 (a) a gene is a section of a chromosome/a chromosome contains many genes (1).

(b) Genes control how different characteristics (1) are developed and passed on to our offspring (1).

(c) Parents produce sex cells/gametes (1); a male and a female gamete are needed to give a complete set of genetic information for offspring (1).

2 (a) variation (1)

(b) The colour of the petals is controlled by genes (1); which the offspring inherit from parent plants (1).

3 (a) average height $= (184 + 191 + 173 + 183 + 195 + 169)/6$ (1) $= 182.5$ cm (1)

(b) Any four from: height determined partly by genes (1); but also depends on environmental factors (1); such as nutrition (1); different children have inherited slightly different genes from their parents (1); parents have different heights so will pass on different genes to their children for height (1); the mean height of the children being above the mean height of the parents could mean that children have better nutrition/they take more after their father than their mother (1).

30. Reproduction

1 (a) (i) asexual reproduction (1)

(ii) There is only one parent (1); the offspring are identical to the parent (1).

(b) It will be the same (1).

2 (a) clones (1)

(b) Plants grown from cuttings have the same (desired) characteristics as the parent plants (1). Also, taking cuttings means that the number of plants that can be produced at the same time is large (1).

3 Sexual reproduction needs two parents/asexual needs only one (1); sexual reproduction needs fertilisation to take place/asexual does not (1); sexual reproduction requires parents to produce gametes/asexual does not (1); in asexual reproduction, offspring are identical to the parent/in sexual reproduction, offspring show variation to the parent (1).

31. Cloning

1 (a) growth medium/rooting powder/compost (1)

(b) Clones are genetically identical to their parent (1).

(c) The callus starts as a small number of cells (1). Through the process of cell division they turn into an adult carrot plant (1).

2 (a) host mother (1)

(b) Any three from: embryo cells are separated from each other (1); at an early stage/before the cells differentiate (1); each embryo cell goes on to divide and form a new embryo (1). Then the following point for the third mark: the process produces identical sheep, which are useful as the farmer has bred sheep with excellent meat yield (1).

3 Any six from: take an egg cell from an adult dog (1); and remove the nucleus/enucleate (1); remove DNA from a body cell of Snuppy's parent (1); insert this DNA into the enucleated egg cell (1); give the cell a mild electric shock (1); to start cell division (1); then transplant this embryo into a host/surrogate mother (1).

32. Genetic engineering

1 (a) The Bt toxin makes the plant resistant to insects/toxic for insects to eat (1). This is useful because the plant will have an increased yield of cotton (1).
   (b) Enzymes are used (1); to take the gene for Bt toxin (1); and insert it into the plant's DNA (1).
2 (a) Eating the rice can increase the vitamin A in the diet (1); which improves the health of people in the country (1).
   (b) The gene that is modified can be transferred from the GM crop into wild rice/non-GM strains of rice (1); where it could affect those crops/have unknown effects (1) OR eating GM crops could have an effect on human health (1); because we do not know what effect the modified gene would have on humans (1).
3 Any four from: GM bacteria produce human insulin not pig insulin (1); so this will be more effective/is the right form of insulin/is less likely to cause adverse reactions (1); can be produced in large quantities by the bacteria (1); this means that it can be produced at low cost (1); also, many people would have ethical objections to having insulin from pigs (1).

33. Issues with new science

1 (a) These goats are rare, so there are few of them in the wild to produce the wool (1). The wool they produce is of high quality, so can be sold for a high price/is expensive (1).
   (b) There are ethical reasons for not cloning humans (1); concerns include worries about humans being cloned to make organs for unwell people/religious principles for people who believe that human life is special (1).
2 The answer needs to have one argument in support of the use of GM animals (1); and one argument against (1); with a conclusion being drawn (1). In support: can lead to cures for serious medical conditions (1); animals are treated with respect and often have normal lives (1). Against: it is cruel/unethical to use animals for this (1); some of the research is not vital to humans/there are other ways of doing it (1). Conclusion statements could include: the overall benefits to humans outweigh ethical concerns (1); overall the use of animals is better than potential alternatives (1); scientists could invest more time in other technologies and avoid using animals (1).
3 (a) this data shows a low level of support for GM food because: nearly half (46%) of people have concerns about GM food (1); whereas only a quarter (25%) do not have those concerns (1).
   (b) There are four marks for this question – three marks are awarded for the arguments you put forward and you must have some arguments in favour and some against in order to score full marks. The final mark is for your conclusion. In favour: GM technology can offer increased yields, to help prevent people starving (1); it can also produce crops that are pest or disease resistant, which also increases yields (1); it can also help meet people's demands for crops that are larger/better coloured/better tasting (1). Against: there are concerns about some artificially inserted genes getting into 'wild' plants (1); some

people are also concerned about the possible effects of eating GM food (1). Your concluding statement should reach a balance between the arguments in favour and those against (1).

34. Evolution

1 (a) toad (1)
   (b) mouse and rat (1)
   (c) They share common characteristics (1); because they evolved separately from a recent common ancestor on a branch of the evolutionary tree (1).
   (d) It shows how similar fossil species changed over time (1).
2 A taller horse can see predators more easily (1); this means it has more time to run away/escape from the predators (1).
3 (a) change in a gene (1); which is random/spontaneous (1)
   (b) Natural selection only takes place when an organism passes on characteristics to offspring (1); and is only seen over many generations (1).
   (c) Disagree (1); some mutations are harmful or fatal (1); and many others have no effect (1).

35. Theories of evolution

1 (a) 1865 (1)
   (b) The number of speckled moths goes down (1). The number of black moths goes up (1).
   (c) There is still some variation/not all trees have darkened so some are still camouflaged/moths change behaviour to be less conspicuous to predators (1).
2 (a) Giraffes had to stretch to reach food in tall trees (1); and so their necks gradually became longer (1); and these long necks were passed on to their offspring (1).
   (b) Any three from: the population of giraffes have variation in neck lengths (1); giraffes with longer necks are better able to find food (1); so they survive longer/are more likely to survive to breed (1); and pass on their genes/characteristics (1).

36. Biology six mark question 3

A basic answer would have a brief description of some of the stages involved in the change to lighter forms.

A good answer would have some description of the stages involved in the change to lighter forms.

An excellent answer would have a clear, balanced description of all the stages involved in a change to lighter forms.

Examples of biology points made in the response:
- in peppered moths there are two different colours (kinds/forms/variants) in the population
- dark/black and speckled or light
- these two forms are controlled by genes
- which the individuals inherit
- the trunks of trees where moths rest in the day are part of their environment
- when these trunks are covered in soot the dark forms are less often eaten by birds
- so they are more likely to survive and reproduce than the light forms
- when soot emissions stopped tree trunks became light again
- so dark forms were now more likely to be seen and eaten by birds
- so they became less likely to survive and reproduce
- and their numbers therefore fell.

Chemistry answers

37. Atoms and elements

1 (a) C and Si (1)   **(b)** Na (1)   **(c)** B and O (1)

2 (a)

Name of particle	Charge	Where found in atom	
proton	positive	in nucleus	(1)
electron	negative	around nucleus	(1)
neutron	no charge/neutral	in nucleus	(1)

(b) The lithium atom is made up of a central nucleus containing three protons (1) and four neutrons (1). Around the nucleus there are three electrons (1).

3 (a) 100 (1). *Anything between 90 and 110 would be accepted.*

(b) An element contains only one kind (1) of atom. A compound contains more than one kind of atom joined (1) together.

38. Particles in atoms

1 (a) The atomic number tells us the number of protons in the nucleus (1). The mass number tells us the number of protons plus neutrons in the nucleus (1).

(b) the atomic number (1)

(c) The atom is neutral as the number of protons equals the number of electrons (1).

2 missing information, upper row: 1, 0 (1); and lower row: V, 23, 51 (1)

3 (a) A and C (1)   **(b)** C (1)

(c) A and C are cobalt, B is nickel and D is copper (1).

4 missing numbers: 17, 37 and 17 (1) and 45, 45 and 51 (1)

39. Electronic structure

1 The number of electrons in each shell should be: 2,8,3 (1); 2,8,7 (1); 2,8,8,2 (1).

2 (a) silicon (1), atomic number = 14 (1)

(b) 14 protons and 14 electrons (1)

(c) the mass number (1)

3 (a) 2,8,8,1 (1)   **(b)** 2,8,5 (1)

4 Missing name: neon (1). The missing atomic numbers are 3 and 10 (1). The electron arrangements in the blank diagrams are 2,8,3 and 2,8 (1). The missing electronic structures are 2,1 and 2,8,3 (1).

40. Electronic structure and groups

1 (a) The element is in group 2 (1) as it has 2 electrons in the highest energy level (1).

(b) The number of electrons in each shell should be: 2,2 (1) and 2,8,2 (1).

(c) Elements in the same group have the same number of electrons in their highest energy level (1).

2 (a) sodium and potassium (1)

(b) neon (1)

3 (a) The melting point increases (1).

(b) Between 140 and 220 °C (1).

(c) $H_2 + Br_2$ (1) $\rightarrow$ 2HBr (1)

41. Making compounds

1 (a) iron + sulfur (1) $\rightarrow$ iron sulfide (1)

(b) The atoms of the elements join together (1) to form a compound.

2 (a) The molecules are formed when the atoms form bonds by sharing electrons (1). These are called covalent bonds (1).

(b) The charged particles are formed by loss and gain of electrons (1). They are called ions (1).

3 Phosphorus chloride and potassium chloride (1); the bonds in phosphorus chloride are formed by sharing electrons (1). The bonds in potassium chloride are formed by loss and gain of electrons (1).

4 (a) The electronic structures are: sodium 2,8,1 (1), and chlorine 2,8,7 (1).

(b) Arrow from single outer electron on sodium to outer shell of chlorine (1).

42. Chemical equations

1 (a) calcium carbonate (1) $\rightarrow$ calcium oxide + carbon dioxide (1)

(b) mass of calcium oxide = 500 − 220 (1) = 280 g (1)

2 (a) 1 molecule of methane reacts with 2 molecules of oxygen (1) to produce 1 molecule of carbon dioxide and 2 molecules of water (1).

(b) mass of products = 11 + 9 = 20 g (1); mass of oxygen = 20 − 4 = 16 g (1)

3 (a) $CH_4 + 2O_2$ (1) $\rightarrow CO_2 + 2H_2O$ (1)

(b) $C_3H_8 + 5O_2$ (1) $\rightarrow 3CO_2 + 4H_2O$ (1)

(c) carbon dioxide (1) and water (1)

4 (a) $4Na + O_2$ (1) $\rightarrow 2Na_2O$ (1). *It is fine to write '1' in front of the O_2 or in front of the CO_2 in Q3(a).*

(b) $4K + O_2$ (1) $\rightarrow 2K_2O$ (1)

43. Limestone

1 Environmental: Quarrying produces a lot of waste/is unsightly/causes pollution in the area. Negative effect: causes environmental problems (1). Social: Quarrying provides work for the local people. This is a positive effect as jobs bring prosperity to an area (1). Economic: Large-scale mining provides work and materials for other businesses. Positive effect as it brings prosperity (1).

2 Solid X is clay (1). Solid Y is sand (1). Solid Z is aggregate (1).

3 Any four from: the main advantages of limestone are that it looks better; doesn't use polluting manufacturing process (1); the disadvantages of limestone are that it is more expensive to use; it is less durable/soft stone and more affected by acid (1). The main advantages of concrete are that it is cheaper; easier to use; resists wear and acid (1); the disadvantages of concrete are that it doesn't look as good; produces pollution in manufacture (1). Plus a valid evaluation such as: limestone may be best for public buildings where appearance is of most importance (1).

44. Calcium carbonate chemistry

1 (a) decomposition (1)

(b) If the limewater turns cloudy/milky (1), then carbon dioxide gas has been produced (1).

(c) copper oxide (1)

2 (a) $CaCO_3(s) + H_2SO_4(aq) \rightarrow CaSO_4(s) + H_2O$ (l) (1) + CO_2 (g) (1)

(b) The calcium sulfate is insoluble (1) and coats the calcium carbonate so acid cannot get at the carbonate (1).

3 (a) Box: calcium oxide (1); add carbon dioxide (1)

(b) limewater (1)

(c) The soil might be too acidic (1) and the calcium oxide would neutralise (1) the acid.

45. Chemistry six mark question 1

A basic answer would give a simple description of how the investigation might be carried out and apparatus that could be used.

A good answer would give a clear description of how the investigation might be carried out, with some details missing e.g. not all variables which need to be controlled listed.

An excellent answer would give a detailed description of all aspects of the investigation – method, results and conclusion, including how the test was made fair and how the results were compared.

Examples of chemistry points made in the response:

- The metal carbonate that decomposes most easily will produce the most carbon dioxide gas in the shortest time.
- Can measure how easily carbonate decomposed by measuring time to turn limewater cloudy enough so cannot see a mark on a paper through it (or other valid method).
- A clearly labelled diagram of the set-up is required (should try to include all the apparatus listed).
- To make the test fair need to keep the following the same: the heat from the Bunsen burner; the type and size of all apparatus; the volume of limewater; the powder size, and mass of the metal carbonate.
- The carbonate that breaks down most easily will make the limewater cloudy in the shortest time.

46. Extracting metals

1 **(a)** Gold and platinum are never found combined as they are very unreactive (1).
  (b) The ore might contain too little metal (1). *You could also say that there might be dangerous impurities in the ore, but this is not in the specification.*
2 **(a)** Copper and tin are easier to extract from their ores than iron (1).
  (b) Extracting aluminium needs electricity (1), which was not available until that time (1).
3 **(a)** reduction (1)
  (b) Iron oxide reacts with carbon (1) to produce iron metal and carbon dioxide (1).
4 **(a)** Aluminium is formed at the negative electrode (1).
  (b) oxygen (1)

47. Extracting copper

1 **(a)** Iron is more reactive than copper (1) and so it displaces copper from copper chloride solution (1).
  (b) iron + copper(II) chloride (1) → copper + iron(II) chloride (1).
  (c) displacement reaction (1)
  (d) zinc chloride (1)
  (e) Scrap iron is cheaper than zinc (1).
2 **(a)** More lower-grade ores are being used as our main reserves of metal ores are running out (1).
  (b) Phytomining uses plants to absorb metals from the soil (1). The plants are then burned and the metal compounds are found in the ash (1). Bioleaching uses bacteria mixed with the metal ores (1) to leach out solutions containing the metal (1) compounds.
  (c) (i) They use less energy than smelting (1).
    (ii) The production of metal is slow (1).

48. Recycling metals

1 **(a)** As no/less new metal ore is needed (1).
  (b) As it reduces the amount of mining, which causes pollution or damages habitats (1).
2 **(a)** aluminium and lead (1)
  (b) 1. Because its ore might be very expensive/running out (1). 2. Because it might be very expensive/difficult to extract the metal (1).
  (c) 72% of 4.6 million = $\frac{72}{100} \times 4.6$ (1) = 3.3 million tonnes (1)
  (d) Any three from: recycling metals saves our finite reserves for the future (1); means less mining and therefore less waste to pollute the environment (1); generates local jobs in collection and processing (1); uses less energy (1); uses less land for landfill (1).
3 **(a)** Stage 1 digs out large amounts of earth to remove ore from the ground (1). Stage 2 produces lots of waste materials, which can be harmful/poisonous to the environment (1).
  (b) Stage 4 needs large amounts of expensive heat energy (1) and electricity (1).

49. Steel and other alloys

1 **(a)** As the carbon content increases the corrosion resistance is unchanged (1), the strength decreases (1) and the hardness increases (1).
  (b) Steel for springs should be strong (1) and flexible (1).
2 **(a)** From top, clockwise labels are: limestone (1) coke (1); and molten iron (1).
  (b) Iron oxide + carbon (1) → iron + carbon dioxide (1)
  (c) The cast iron has limited uses as it is very brittle (1) and it would break rather than bend (1).

50. Transition metals

1 **(a)** Any two metals from the central block of the Periodic Table (see page 112), such as titanium, vanadium, iron, gold, silver, etc. (1).
  (b) does not react with water (1); good conductor of electricity (1); good conductor of heat (1)
2 **(a)** It is less dense/lighter (1), and it does not rust (1).
  (b) It is cheaper (1).
  (c) Croalumin is the best choice as it has a low density (1), high melting point *(as aircraft bodies will, at times, experience high temperatures)* (1) and a good resistance to corrosion (1).
3 Any four from the following, plus valid evaluation. Advantages of wood: lighter/less dense (1); does not rust (1); often available in the local area (1); easily cut into shape (1). Advantages of steel: stronger (1); does not rot (1). Evaluation: wood is better for a small structure in remote area as easier to transport (1).

51. Hydrocarbons

1 **A** mixture and elements (1); **B** pure and compound (1); **C** pure and element (1); **D** mixture and compound (1)
2 **(a)** Fossil fuels are fuels made from the remains of living things which died millions of years ago (1). Hydrocarbons are compounds of carbon and hydrogen **only** (1). *You must make it clear that hydrocarbons do not contain any elements other than hydrogen and carbon to get the mark.*
  (b) (i) methane (1)
    (ii) between −88 and −1°C (1)
    (iii) C_3H_8 (1)

(c)

(1)

52. Crude oil and alkanes

1 (a) C_{10}/C_{11} to C_{13}/C_{14} (1)

(b) (i) residue (1)

(ii) fuel gases (1)

(iii) petrol (1)

2 (a) The crude oil is heated until most of it has evaporated (1). It then passes into a fractionating (1) column. As the mixture of gases rise (1) up the tower the gases cool and condense (1) back to liquids.

(b) (i) A and B (1)

(ii) E (1)

3 A low viscosity is important as it means that the liquid runs easily and can flow through pipes (1). A high flammability is important as it means the fuel catches fire easily (1).

53. Combustion

1 (a) In test tube A, a colourless liquid forms (1). In test tube B, the limewater turns from clear/colourless to cloudy/milky (1).

(b) ethanol + oxygen (1) → carbon dioxide + water (1)

2 (a) carbon monoxide and carbon (1)

(b) carbon dioxide – global warming/climate change (1), carbon monoxide – poisonous (1); carbon – soot makes buildings dirty/causes lung damage (1)

3 (a) the air (1); burning sulfur in fuel (1).

(b) 2 % (1)

(c) Sulfur dioxide causes acid rain (1), which damages living things/corrodes buildings and metals (1).

54. Biofuels

1 (a) Biofuels are made from material from living things (1).

(b) The source of hydrogen will not run out (1).

(c) Coal is a solid so doesn't need special gas containers/ hydrogen can escape easier as it is a gas/coal does not explode if it escapes from its container (1).

(d) Petrol comes from crude oil, which was made from tiny living things that died millions of years ago (1).

(e) During photosynthesis (1) plants make sugars by removing carbon dioxide from the air (1) so when ethanol, made from sugar, burns, the carbon dioxide produced replaces the carbon dioxide removed (1).

2 (a) The only product of combustion is water (1).

(b) The electricity from the National Grid is mostly produced using fossil fuels (1), which produce polluting gases when they burn (1).

3 (a) Advantage: biodiesel is renewable/has less effect on the atmosphere than diesel (1). Disadvantage: growing plants to make biodiesel wastes space to grow crops for food/makes food more expensive/ biodiesel is in short supply (1).

(b) Advantage: more resources of coal/easier to store (1). Disadvantage: coal is dirty/harder to move solid fuel into engine (1).

(c) Advantage: hydrogen is renewable/non-polluting when burned in car engines (1). Disadvantage: hydrogen is in short supply/storage more difficult/ still needs electricity to make it (1).

55. Chemistry six mark question 2

A basic answer would give a simple description of an advantage **and/or** a disadvantage of petrol and ethanol.

A good answer would give a clear description of both advantages **and** disadvantages of petrol ethanol. Clear references are made to **one or two** of the issues, economic, ethical or environmental.

An excellent answer would give a detailed description of both advantages **and** disadvantages of petrol and ethanol. References are made to a wide range of issues.

Examples of chemistry points made in the response:

- Petrol is made from crude oil, which is running out.
- Ethanol can be made by the fermentation of sugar, which is a renewable resource.
- There are other important products made from crude oil (medicines, plastics, etc.)
- Ethanol is useful in countries with limited oil supplies.
- Producing ethanol from plants is time consuming and labour intensive.
- The use of land to grow crops to make ethanol takes land that could be used for crops.
- This makes food supplies short or increases the price of food.
- Using fossil fuels causes pollution (acid rain) and increases greenhouse gases.
- Burning ethanol is cleaner and, if made using renewable resources, is carbon neutral.

56. Cracking and alkenes

1 (a) $C_6H_{14} \rightarrow C_4H_{10} + C_2H_4$ (1)

(b) C_nH_{2n+2} (1)

(c) (i) alkenes (1)

(ii) Add bromine water (1); if an unsaturated hydrocarbon is present the solution quickly goes from brown to colourless (1). *You do not get the mark if you say the solution goes clear – clear solutions can still be coloured.*

2 (a) B and D (1)

(b) C propane (1); D ethene (1)

3 (a) B (1); as it has the most bitumen, which is thickest (1).

(b) Cracking would increase the amount of fuel gas/ petrol (1) and reduce the amount of bitumen/fuel oil (1).

57. Making polymers

1 (a) ethene (1) and poly(ethene) (1)

(b) Polymers are long (chain) molecules (1) made by joining many small molecules (1) together.

(c) Any two from: strong; flexible; waterproof; rot-proof (2).

2 (a)

For correct number of carbon atoms (1), for correct number of hydrogens (1), for one C=C double bond (1).

(b) 3 (1)

3 (a) Reusable packaging/memory foam mattresses/ aircraft seats (1), as it returns to its original shape (1).

(b) Rainwear (1), as it would keep you dry and comfortable/ keep rain out and also let sweat out, etc. (1).

58. Polymer problems

1 (a) When thrown away Biopol would eventually rot away (1) and not cause pollution problems/fill up landfill sites (1).
(b) If left unused for a long time biodegradable bottles might start to degrade or people might think that the container will rot away too soon (1).
2 Advantage for the economy: Recycling saves money in buying raw materials/provides jobs in the recycling industry (1). Advantage for our environment: recycling means less plastic thrown away so less pollution/litter (1). Advantage for the use of resources: recycling saves oil resources (1).
3 (a) $8 + 41 + 18 + 11 + 8$ (or $100 - 3 - 11$) (1) $= 86\%$ (1)
(b) We will need to find alternative energy sources (1). We will need to find new sources of chemicals (for petrochemicals) (1).

59. Ethanol

1 (a) ethene + steam → ethanol (1)
(b) hydration (1)
2 (a) Yeast (1) is added to sugar solution (1) and left. The products are ethanol and carbon dioxide (1).
(b) It is renewable (1) as it is formed from sugar from plants, which can be grown again (1).
(c) as a fuel (1); as a drink (1)
3 Ethanol from ethene uses up non-renewable resources of crude oil (1). Ethanol from sugar cane uses renewable resources of plants (1).
4 $C_2H_5OH \rightarrow C_2H_4 + H_2O$ (1); ethanol → ethene + water (1)

60. Vegetable oils

1 (a) In X the water boils to form steam (1) and the oil is vaporised/removed (1) (from the crushed olives). In Y the oil and water vapour mixture is cooled (1) and condenses/turns back to a liquid (1).
(b) Two layers form as the oil and water do not mix (1).
(c) Separating funnel (1).
2 (a) In oil, food cooks at a higher temperatures (1), so it cooks faster (1). It also has a higher energy content (1).
(b) Oils and fats both supply energy (1); both can lead to weight problems (1); oils are better for health than fats (1).

61. Emulsions

1 (a) Any two from: paints; cosmetic creams; ice cream (2).
(b) Emulsifiers in foods produce better textures/ appearances (1) but incorporate fats and oils into foods, which makes their energy content high/allergy to eggs (1).
2 (a) An emulsion is formed by mixing oil (1) and water (1) with the addition of an emulsifier/emulifying agent (1).
(b) Oil droplets

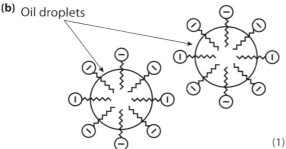

(1)

One end of each emulsifying agent molecule is hydrophobic and dissolves in the oil (1) and the other end is hydrophilic and dissolves in the water (1). The emulsifier molecules surround the oil droplets and stop them joining together again (1).

62. Hardening plant oils

1 (a) Fats have higher melting points and are usually solids while oils are liquids (1). Oils contain more unsaturated molecules than fats (1). Both oils and fats provide the body with energy (1). It is thought a diet high in fats can cause health problems (1).
(b) Add bromine water (1), if double bonds are present then it changes from brown to colourless (1).
2 (a) Oils and fats with a high saturated content have higher melting points than oils with a lower saturated content (1).
(b) Oils and fats with a lower saturated content have slightly higher energy values than oils and fats with a higher saturated content (1).
(c) monounsaturated – single double bond (1) and polyunsaturated – lots of double bonds (1).
3 (a) margarine (1)
(b) The double bond is removed (1) by adding on hydrogen (1).

63. The Earth's structure

1 (a) From middle right clockwise: core (1), mantle (1) and crust (1).
(b) the atmosphere (1) and the crust (1)
2 (a) The crust (1) and the upper part of the mantle (1) are cracked into large pieces (1), which are called tectonic plates.
(b) Sudden movements of the tectonic plates (1) as one plate moves over another (1) cause earthquakes.
(c) volcanoes/mountains (1)
3 (a) Convection currents (1) produced by heat (1) (in the mantle) cause the plates to move.
(b) They would move away from each other by a few centimetres (1) in one year.
(c) When two objects rub together there is friction which makes it difficult for them to move against each other (1). The pressure increases and when it reaches a certain point, the force of friction is overcome very suddenly (1), but scientists cannot predict when this will happen (1).

64. Continental drift

1 (a) The shapes (1) of South America and Africa fit together (1).
(b) It was shown that rock formations (1) and fossils (1) of living things were similar in South America and Africa.
2 (a) Wegener's theory does not explain how the continents (1) can move through or over the ocean beds (1), which he thought were fixed in place.
(b) As continents moved towards each other (1), the crust was pushed up (1) where they met, to form mountains.
(c) They thought that mountains were formed due to shrinking of the Earth's crust (1) as the Earth cooled down (1).

65. The Earth's atmosphere

1 (a) nitrogen, oxygen and 20% (2)
(b) argon (1)

2 (a) The gases in air have different boiling points (1), so if it is turned into a liquid air can be separated by distillation (1).
   (b) (i) nitrogen (1)
      (ii) oxygen and nitrogen (1)
3 (a) Temperatures need to be the same as gas volumes change with temperature (1).
   (b) $2Mg + O_2 \rightarrow 2MgO$ (1 mark for correct symbols and 1 mark for balancing)
   (c) oxygen used up $= 200 - 172 = 28$
      $\therefore$ % oxygen $= \frac{28}{200} \times 100$ (1) $= 14\%$ (1)
   (d) The calculated percentage of oxygen might have been less than the actual value as not enough magnesium was used/some magnesium remained unreacted (1) and some oxygen was not used up (1).

66. The early atmosphere and life

1 (a) They thought that the early atmosphere was formed by volcanic action (1).
   (b) The water vapour in the air cooled and condensed to form the oceans (1).
2 (a) carbon dioxide (1); and any two from: water (1), ammonia (1), methane (1) or sulfur dioxide (1)
   (b) (i) the oceans (1)
      (ii) lightning (1)
3 (a) Because the other planets (in our solar system) would have been formed about the same time (1) as the Earth from the same materials (1).
   (b) The Earth's early atmosphere was produced by volcanoes (1), which release large amounts of carbon dioxide gas, the main gas in the atmosphere of Venus (1).
   (c) The Earth was formed a long time ago (1). Scientists do not have a sample of the early atmosphere to analyse (1).

67. Evolution of the atmosphere

1 (a) Compared with the modern atmosphere the early atmosphere contained no oxygen and very little nitrogen (1). There was also more carbon dioxide (1) and about the same amount of argon (1).
   (b) Today's atmosphere will be analysed accurately (1). Scientists had to guess what the early Earth atmosphere was like (1).
   (c) As algae and plants photosynthesise (1), they take in carbon dioxide gas (1) and give out oxygen (1).
2 (a) Cooling formed oceans (1) which dissolved carbon dioxide (1).
   (b) $H_2O(l) + CO_2(aq)$ (1) $\rightarrow H_2CO_3(aq)$
   (c) (i) Shellfish use up carbon dioxide (1).
      (ii) They eventually form carbonate rocks/limestone (1).

68. Carbon dioxide today

1 (a) During photosynthesis plants take in carbon dioxide (1) so if there are fewer plants (trees) then less carbon dioxide is removed from the atmosphere (1).
   (b) Increased burning of fossil fuels (1) gives out more carbon dioxide (1).
   (c) Increased levels of carbon dioxide are thought to increase global/average temperatures (1), and when dissolved in water it makes the water acidic (1).
2 (a) As carbon dioxide levels increase, the average world temperature increases (1). As carbon dioxide levels decrease, the average world temperature decreases (1).

   (b) The trend shows even larger increases in carbon dioxide levels (1), which could mean larger increases in average temperatures (1).
3 (a) The rise in mean surface temperatures due to the increasing amounts of greenhouse gases such as carbon dioxide (1).
   (b) Any two from: polar ice caps melt; more deserts; changes in climates; rising sea levels (2).

69. Chemistry six mark question 3

A basic answer: There is a simple description of one change that governments/local authorities **and/or** one that groups of people could make to reduce global warming.

A good answer: There is a clear description of one change that governments/local authorities **and** one that groups of people, could make to reduce global warming.

An excellent answer: There is a detailed description **and** explanation of one change that governments/local authorities, **and** one that groups of people could make to reduce global warming. The description includes a comment on the probability of success of the proposed changes.

Examples of chemistry points made in the response:
- Greenhouse gases like carbon dioxide increase global warming.
- Carbon dioxide is produced by burning most fuels.
- Renewable fuels/biofuels can be carbon neutral.
- Hydrogen produced using renewable resources is non-polluting.
- Possible changes made by governments/local authorities: influencing international conferences on climate change; passing laws to ban the use of certain fuels by different groups; increasing taxes to make certain fuels less economic to use; organising advertising campaigns to cut down use of fuels; banning less efficient boilers/engines.
- Possible changes made by groups of individuals: sharing cars; increasing use of public transport; cutting down on energy uses in home; improving insulation; cutting down speed when driving.
- Governments/local authorities should be able to force changes on the whole country, which will therefore generally have more effect than small groups of individuals.

Physics answers

70. Infrared radiation

1 White/light coloured T-shirts would be best (1), as they will reflect infrared radiation and help to keep him cool (1).
2 Line B is for the black cup (1). Objects with black surfaces will cool down faster as these surfaces are better emitters of heat radiation than white surfaces (1).
3 (a) Any four from: the 'Hot Stuff' heater will radiate more heat as dull, black surfaces are better radiators than light, shiny surfaces (1), and it will also radiate more heat as it has a larger surface area (1). The 'Cosy Comfort' heater is cheaper (1) and she may prefer the appearance of a white heater (1). She needs to decide whether heating, cost or appearance is the most important (1).
   (b) It will increase (1), because hotter objects emit more radiation in a given time than cooler objects (1).

71. Kinetic theory

1 (a) A – solid, B – liquid, C – gas (2)

(b) The bonds between the particles break apart (1) and the particles start moving past each other (1).

2 (a) Flour and sand can both be poured (1) and they take the shape of the container they are in (1).

(b) The particles within each piece of flour/grain of sand are in fixed positions (1), so each piece has a fixed shape (1).

(c) As the particles are heated to 1000 °C they gain more energy (1), but they are still held in a fixed arrangement (1). At 2000 °C the particles have even more energy/ more energy than at 1000 °C (1), but they will not be in fixed positions because the sand is now a liquid (1).

72. Methods of transferring energy

1 (a) conduction (1)

(b) When the wax near the bottom of the lamp is heated, it expands and becomes less dense (1). The wax rises (1) in the lamp. At the top of the lamp, the wax loses energy/cools down (1). It becomes denser and sinks (1).

2 (a) In conduction, vibrations are passed on from particle to particle (1). Particles in a solid are very close together so the vibrations can easily be passed on/ particles in a gas move around rather than vibrate (1).

(b) Metals have free electrons (1), which can transfer energy (1).

3 (a) It stops the water from the sand contaminating the food (1).

(b) Water that has moved through the pot will evaporate (1). The particles that evaporate have more energy than the particles that are left behind (1), so the temperature of the water left behind falls (1).

73. Rate of energy transfer

1 (a) Plastic bung – good insulator reduces energy transfer by conduction (1) and also by convection from the surface of the liquid (1). Inner silver mirror – reflects radiation back into the hot liquid (1). Vacuum – poor conductor (1).

(b) The flask reduces the amount of energy transferred (1), so it can reduce the amount of energy being transferred into the flask as well as the amount being transferred out (1).

2 (a) Energy is transferred from your body to the air around you (1), so this air will warm up (1). The warm air will become less dense and will rise/the warmed air will be moved away by convection (1).

(b) On a windy day the air warmed by your body will be blown away faster than it will move away on a still day (1), so there will be a bigger temperature difference between your body and the surrounding air (1), the rate at which energy is transferred by heating will be greater and you will feel colder (1).

3 Any four from: sweating helps to keep us cool when it evaporates (1), but water vapour in the air can also condense onto our skin (1). On a dry day, there is not much water vapour in the air to condense, so sweat evaporates quickly (1). On a humid day, water vapour can condense as fast as it evaporates (1) so our skin stays wet and we do not cool by sweating (1).

74. Keeping warm

1 (a) £6000/£120 (1) = 50 years (1)

(b) It is cheaper (1) and the payback time is less (1).

2 (a) Plastic is a better insulating material than metal (1). The lower the U-value, the less energy is transferred by heating (1), so plastic windows should have lower U-values than metal-framed windows (1).

(b) The householder's current windows are type C. Changing to plastic frames changes the U-value from 3.7 to 3.1, so a decrease of 0.6 (1). Changing from a 6 mm to a 12 mm gap decreases the U-value by 0.3 (1). So changing the material of the frames will make the greatest difference (1).

75. Specific heat capacity

1 Brick has a high specific heat capacity (1) so can absorb lots of energy (1).

2 temperature change = 40 °C (1);
energy = 100 kg × 40 °C × 900 J/kg °C (1) = 3 600 000 J (1)

3 (a) temperature change = 35 °C (1);
$c = E/(m \times \theta) = 15\,000/(1 \times 35)$ (1) = 429 (1) J/kg °C (1)

(b) Some of the energy transferred to the metal block was transferred to the surroundings (1), so the value for energy used in the calculation was higher than it should be (1).

(c) The student who heats the block for the shortest time will obtain the most accurate value (1) because if the block is heated for a shorter time, less of the energy transferred to it will be transferred on to the surroundings (1).

76. Energy and efficiency

1 Efficiency = 10 J/100 J × 100% (1) = 10% (1)

2 (a) Wasted energy = 1000 J − 900 J = 100 J (1)

(b) efficiency = 900 J/1000 J × 100% (1) = 90% (1)

3 (a) useful power = 0.9 × 750 W = 675 W (1);
wasted power = 750 W − 675 W = 75 W (1) OR wasted power = 0.1 × 750 W (1) = 75 W (1)

(b) Sankey diagram with one output arrow 9 times as wide as the other (1), large output arrow labelled 'kinetic energy' and 'energy transferred by heating' (1), and small output arrow labelled 'sound energy' (1). *You could also label the smaller arrow 'energy heating the body of the hairdryer'.*

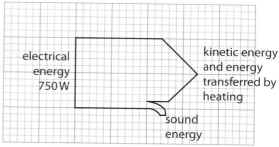

(c) Energy transferred by the hot air is useful (1), but energy transferred to the body of the hairdryer (and to the surroundings) is wasted energy (1).

77. Physics six mark question 1

A basic answer will give a brief description of several features that reduce energy transfer.

A good answer will give a clear description of several features that reduce energy transfer with a detailed explanation of at least one of them.

An excellent answer will give a clear and detailed description of all the features that reduce energy transfer with a detailed description of several of them.

ANSWERS

Examples of physics points made in the response:

Double glazing:
- Two panes of glass with space in-between filled with gas.
- Both the glass and the gas in-between are poor conductors.

Cavity wall insulation:
- Gap between walls is filled with a foam.
- Both foam and the air it contains are poor conductors so less energy is lost through conduction.

Blinds and shiny curtains:
- Reflect radiation back into the room.
- Also poor conductors so less energy lost through conduction.

Draught excluders:
- Stop energy being lost by convection.

Loft insulation:
- Insulating material placed underneath roof.
- Insulating material is poor conductor so less energy lost through conduction.

78. Electrical appliances

1 power in kW = 0.75 (1); cost (in pence) = power (in kW) × time (in hours) × cost per unit (in pence); cost (in pence) = 0.75 × 0.5 × 12 (1); cost (in pence) = 4.5p (1)
2 energy transferred = 3000 W × (5 × 60) seconds (1) = 900 000 J (or 900 kJ) (1)
3 45 minutes = 45/60 hours = 0.75 hours (1); energy transferred = 2.4 kW × 0.75 hours (1) = 1.8 kWh (1)
4 30 745 − 29 638 = 1107 units (1); cost = 1107 × 14p = £154.98 (1)
5 cost per unit $= \dfrac{\text{cost}}{(\text{power} \times \text{time})} = \dfrac{160\text{p}}{(2\text{ kW} \times 5\text{ hours})}$ (1) = 16p per unit (1)

79. Choosing appliances

1 (a) sandwich toaster: 600 W × 64% = 384 W (1); microwave: 800 W × 95% = 760 W (1); electric grill: 1400 W × 32% = 448 W (1); toaster: 1000 W × 88% = 880 W (1)
(b) microwave (1) because it has the highest fficiency (1)
(c) microwave (1)
(d) (i) useful power per £ for the grill = 448 W/£40 = 11.2 W/£ (1); useful power per £ for the toaster = 880 W/£18 = 49 W/£ (1)
(ii) You can only make toast in a toaster/you can cook more things using a grill than with a toaster (1).
2 Any three from: The microwave would be the most suitable (1). If a meal typically takes half an hour to cook, it would use 850 × 30 × 60 = 1 530 000 J (1). If the slow cooker takes 8 hours to cook a meal, it would use 100 × 8 × 60 × 60 = 2 880 000 J (1). Also, using the slow cooker would mean that the generator would have to be kept running for 8 hours, when it may not be needed for anything else (1).

80. Generating electricity

1 burned (1), natural gas (1), atmosphere/environment (1)
2 (a) The fuel is burned and the energy is used to produce steam (1). The steam makes turbines spin (1), and the turbines drive generators (1).
(b) Advantages: nuclear fuels do not release carbon dioxide or sulfur dioxide (1). This means there is less air pollution (1). *You could also say that nuclear fuels are more plentiful than fossil fuels.* Disadvantages:

waste produced is radioactive (1). This makes it difficult and expensive to dispose of (1). *You could also say that nuclear power stations are expensive to build and decommission.*
3 Any four from: the information in the table favours gas over coal or nuclear, as the power station is cheaper to build and produces cheaper electricity (1). Although the gas power station does not last as long, it costs £23/kW/year compared with £40/kW/year for a coal power station and £50\kW\year for nuclear, so gas is still a better choice (1). Burning gas produces less air pollution than burning coal, but nuclear power stations do not pollute the air, so from this point of view nuclear would be better (1). Nuclear fuels will last far longer than fossil fuels, but supplies of fossil fuels are likely to last as long as the next batch of power stations to be built, so this is not really an argument either way (1). Burning all fossil fuels adds carbon dioxide to the atmosphere, whereas nuclear power stations do not, so this point would favour nuclear power stations (1).

81. Renewables

1 (a) The turbine starts to generate electricity when the wind is blowing at about 15 km/h (1). As the wind speed increases the turbine generates more electricity up to a maximum of 500 MW (1). When the wind is blowing at more than 90 km/h the amount of electricity generated decreases very quickly (1).
(b) The wind does not blow all the time (1), and the turbines would not generate any electricity when the wind is not blowing (1).
2 Advantages: no greenhouse gases produced (1); renewable energy resource/fuel will not run out (1). Disadvantages: does not work at night or when it isn't sunny (unreliable) (1); expensive (1).
3 Any four from: even if night-time electricity is cheaper, people will never want to use as much electricity at night as during the day (1); many businesses are only open during they day so they cannot use night-time electricity (1); a pumped storage power station needs two reservoirs at different levels; and there are not many suitable locations in the UK (1); some energy will be wasted pumping water up and letting it run down again (or energy is wasted in the transmission lines sending the electricity to and from the pumped storage power station) (1); so this method will still waste some electricity (1).

82. Environment and energy

1 Hydroelectric schemes do not produce carbon dioxide or sulfur dioxide (1), but they do require that land is flooded and can harm wildlife (1). Fossil fuel power stations need less land (1), but they produce more waste gases (1).
2 Arguments for building the wind farm: the energy source is renewable (1) and it does not release polluting/greenhouse gases (1). Arguments against building the wind farm: the turbines will cause visual pollution (1) and the turbines will cause noise pollution when they are generating electricity OR building access roads/maintaining the turbines will disturb habitats/wildlife (1).
3 (a) Carbon dioxide produced from burning fossil fuels is collected (1) and stored in old oil and gas fields (1).
(b) CCS reduces the amount of carbon dioxide in the atmosphere (1), which reduces the greenhouse effect/global warming (1), so the people concerned about the environment are more likely to be in favour of CCS (1).
(c) Any two from: CCS schemes encourage the burning of fossil fuels (as harm to the environment is reduced), so

might mean our supplies of fossil fuels run out faster (1). It is costly, so electricity from power stations using CCS will be more expensive (1). It is unproven – it is possible that the carbon dioxide could leak out of its storage, which would create a more sudden/bigger problem in the future (1).

4 (a) Biofuels are mostly made from plants, which absorbed carbon dioxide from the air when they grew (1), so when they are burned they are only releasing the same amount of carbon dioxide that they originally absorbed (1).

(b) Any three from: energy is needed to make fertiliser (1), harvest the crops (1), and turn them into biofuels (1). And for the third mark: Unless this energy comes from renewable resources, the energy needed to produce the biofuels will add carbon dioxide to the atmosphere (1).

83. Distributing electricity

1 Increasing the voltage reduces the current (1), and this reduces the power transferred as heat in the transmission lines (1).

2 A – step-up transformer (1), B – 400 kV (1), C – transmission lines (1), D – step-down transformer (1), E – step-down transformer (1), F – 230 V (1). *Note: B and C can be either way round.*

3 Any three from: overhead power lines are cheaper to build than underground cables (1), and also cheaper to maintain (1), but many people think they look bad/cause visual pollution (1). There is more disruption to habitats when power lines are being buried than when pylons are constructed (1). Underground lines are safer than overhead power lines because they cannot be touched by kite strings, etc. (1).

84. Physics six mark question 2

A basic answer would include a brief description of an advantage or disadvantage of either a nuclear power station or a coal-fired power station.

A good answer would include a description of some advantages and disadvantages of both a nuclear power station and a coal-fired power station.

An excellent answer would include a clear, balanced and detailed description of the advantages and disadvantages of both a nuclear power station and a coal-fired power station.

Examples of physics points made in the response:
Advantages of nuclear:
- large amounts of electrical energy produced per kg of fuel
- no greenhouse gases produced by burning fossil fuels
- does not pollute the atmosphere under normal working conditions
- supplies of nuclear fuel will last much longer than fossil fuels.

Disadvantages of nuclear:
- highly dangerous if an accident occurs, leading to diseases such as cancer for many people
- huge areas of land can be left uninhabitable for many years after a disaster
- possible contamination issues involving nuclear waste buried underground or at sea
- radioactive waste needs to be disposed of or stored, waste remains radioactive for many years
- high set-up and decommissioning costs
- non-renewable
- threat and implications of terrorist attack
- security problems – nuclear material being stolen to make nuclear weapons.

Advantages of coal:
- accidents will not produce nuclear radiation
- faster start-up time
- lower set-up costs.

Disadvantages of coal:
- contributes to the greenhouse effect/global warming
- less efficient/more fuel needed to generate same amount of electricity
- non-renewable, and will run out before nuclear fuel.

85. Properties of waves

1 (a) Sketch of transverse wave (1), amplitude (1) and wavelength (1) correctly marked.

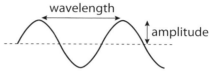

(b) A compression is where particles are closer together than normal (1). A rarefaction is where particles are further apart than normal (1).

(c) It is a longitudinal wave because the particles vibrate in the same direction as the energy is being transferred (1). It is a mechanical wave because it needs a medium to travel through/it cannot travel in a vacuum (1).

2 frequency = number of waves per second = 12 waves/60 seconds (1); frequency = 0.2 Hz (1)

3 speed = 40 000 Hz × 0.0085 m (1) = 340 m/s (1)

4 wavelength = 50 cm = 0.5 m (1); frequency = speed/wavelength = 5130 m/s/0.5 m (1) = 10,260 Hz (1)

86. Electromagnetic waves

1 (a) They all travel at the same speed in a vacuum (1). They are all transverse waves (1).

(b) (i) 10^{-15} m (1)

(ii) 10^4 m (or 10 000 m) (1)

(c) Gamma rays have a higher frequency than radio waves (1); gamma rays transfer more energy than radio waves (1).

2 (a) radio and TV broadcasts (1)

(b) remote controls (1)

(c) photography/optical fibres (1)

(d) transmitting mobile phone signals (1)

3 (a) Find a group of people who have been using mobile phones for many years, and a similar group of people who do not use mobile phones (1) and see if there is any difference in the numbers of them suffering from cancers or other problems that might be caused by mobile phones (1). *Other similar answers would be acceptable, such as monitoring the two groups for several years to see if their rates of illness are different.* OR Collect information on how the number of mobile phones in use in a country/area/population has changed over a number of years (1) and compare this with the rates of cancer (or other problems that might have been caused by mobile phone use) in the same population over the same time (1).

(b) Any two from: people become ill for many reasons, and if the effect of mobile phones is small it may not show up (1); any harm caused by mobile phones may take many years to appear, so a study might have to last a long time (1); many studies rely on people estimating how much they use their phones, and these estimates may not be very accurate (1); it could be very difficult to find a control group of people who never use mobile phones (1); the technology in mobile phones is improving all the time, so even if early phones were harmful, modern ones may not be and this would confuse results (1).

87. Waves

1 (a) (i) Line reflects with angles of incidence and reflection approximately equal (1), with an arrow on the reflected ray to show its direction of travel (1).

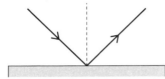

(ii) reflection (1)

(b) (i) Line enters glass at an angle closer to the normal (1).

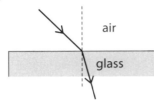

(ii) refraction (1)

(c) It would enter the glass without changing direction (1).

2 (a) Buoys 4 and 5 would be affected (1), because waves could come straight into the harbour/they will be affected whether or not the waves are diffracted (1).

(b) 1 and 6 (1), because these will only be affected if the waves are diffracted through the gap (1) and the most diffraction happens when the wavelength of waves is about the same size as the gap (1).

(c) All the buoys except 1 and 6 could be affected on days when the wavelength of the waves is a bit less (1) or a bit more than 15 metres (1) because there will not be as much diffraction (1). *If the wavelength is a lot less or a lot more than 15 metres buoys 2, 3 and 6 may not be affected as there will not be very much diffraction at all.*

88. Reflection in mirrors

1 (a) Lines from candle extended to mirror and reflecting off it (1) with the angles of reflection equal to the angles of incidence (1). Dashed lines extending behind the mirror to show the position of the image (1).

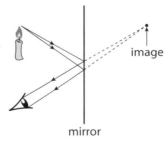

(b) upright (1), virtual (1)

2 (a) Light ray coming from back of car with arrowhead to show direction of travel (1), light ray going from mirror to the driver, with arrowhead to show direction of travel (1), mirror drawn so that the angles of incidence and reflection are equal (1).

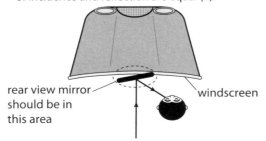

rear view mirror should be in this area   windscreen

(b) The angle of the mirror will only allow the driver to see his/her own face OR light from behind the vehicle will no longer be reflected towards the driver's eyes (1).

3 2 separate incident rays drawn (1), each ray reflected by both mirrors (1) with angles of incidence and reflection equal (1) and arrows on rays to show direction of movement (1).

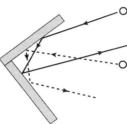

89. Sound

1 (a) As the frequency increases, the pitch increases/A sound with a high (low) frequency has a high (low) pitch (1).

(b) As the amplitude of a sound wave increases, the loudness increases/A sound with a large (small) amplitude will be loud (quiet) (1).

2 The sound wave travels to the cliff and is reflected off the cliff (1). The sound takes 2 seconds to travel to the cliff and back again (1).

3 (a) X is the amplitude of the wave (1). This represents the maximum displacement of air particles from their original position as the wave passes (1).

(b) (i) Waves with a smaller amplitude (1) but the same distance between crests (1) as shown in the diagram.

(ii) A quieter sound has a lower amplitude, so the waves on the oscilloscope screen will not be as tall (1).

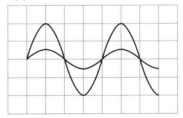

90. Red-shift

1 Siren A is stationary/not moving (1) because the waves are evenly spaced around the siren (1). Siren B is moving towards person B (1) because the waves by person B are closer together than they are on the side opposite to person B (1).

2 Galaxy X is moving away from the Earth faster than Galaxy Y (1); because the lines are shifted further towards the red end of the spectrum/the light shows more red-shift (1). This means that Galaxy X is further away than Galaxy Y (1), because the more distant galaxies are moving away faster than closer ones/the greater the distance the greater the speed (1).

3 Any two from: red-shift is radiation at longer wavelengths than normal (1). The light from the star could be red-shifted, but we don't know this unless we know what the light from a stationary star looks like (1), and some stars are naturally red (1).

91. The expanding Universe

1 (a) S (1)   **(b)** S (1)   **(c)** P (1)

2 (a) As the distance of a galaxy from Earth increases the speed of the galaxy increases (1).

(b) Hubble's graph suggests that the size of the Universe is increasing (1).

3 (a) Cosmic microwave background radiation (CMBR) (1).

(b) The Big Bang theory predicted that the radiation from the Big Bang (1) would have been red-shifted into the microwave region of the electromagnetic spectrum (1). CMBR provided the evidence (1).

4 (a) It is the only theory that can explain the CMBR (1). *You could also say that it explains the most observations.*

(b) A new model might be developed that explains why the expansion is getting faster (as well as explaining everything that the Big Bang theory explains) (1) OR new evidence might be discovered that the Big Bang theory cannot explain, so scientists would develop a new model (1).

92. Physics six mark question 3

A basic answer would include a brief description of the similarities *or* differences of microwaves and infrared waves *or* a common use.

A good answer would include a description of the similarities *and* differences of microwaves and infrared waves, *and* a common use.

An excellent answer would include a clear and detailed description of the similarities *and* differences of microwaves and infrared waves and a common use.

Examples of physics points made in the response:
Similarities:
- are both transverse waves
- can both be reflected, refracted or diffracted
- both travel at speed of light in a vacuum
- neither are detected by the eyes.

Differences:
- infrared has shorter wavelength than microwaves
- infrared has a higher frequency than microwaves
- infrared has higher energy than microwaves
- infrared cooks food from the outside in and microwaves cook food from the inside out.

Uses:
- both microwaves and infrared are used for cooking
- both are used for communications, e.g. microwaves used in mobile phones and satellites, infrared used in remote controls for TVs.

Practice paper answers

Science A Biology B1 practice paper

1 (a) tissues (1)
(b) clinical (1)
(c) placebo (1)
(d) morning sickness (1), limb deformities/birth defects (1)

2 (a) The oxygen content drops to zero (1) and then gradually rises back to its original level (1).
(b) Worm/tubifex (1); red-tailed maggot (1).

3 Any two pairs from: ingest/take in/engulf pathogen (1) *(Note: 'eat' would not be allowed)*, which kill it/break it down/destroy it (1); produce antibodies (1), which destroy pathogen (1); produce antitoxins (1), which cancel counteract poisons/toxins from pathogen (1).

4 (a) steam heat/autoclave (1); passed through a flame (1)
(b) prevents the transfer of unwanted microorganisms/kills unwanted microorganisms (1)
(c) with adhesive tape (1)
(d) in a thermostatically controlled incubator (1)
(e) to stop/reduce likelihood of growth human pathogens (1)
(f) kills bacteria (1)

5 Any four from: shoot has bent away from gravity, root has bent toward it (1); in shoot and root auxin built up on underside due to movement down (1); in shoot high levels of auxin stimulate cell elongation (1); causing bending upwards (1); in roots low levels of auxin stimulate cell elongation (1); causing bending downwards (1).

6 A basic answer would give a description where either one organism (plants, animals or microorganisms) or one process is named.

A good answer would give a description in which micro-organisms and photosynthesis and respiration are named.

An excellent answer would give a description that names microorganisms and explains their role in decomposition as well as describing photosynthesis by plants and respiration in plants, animals and microorganisms.

Examples of biology points made in the response:
- Respiration in plants, animals and microorganisms releases carbon dioxide as it breaks down carbon compounds.
- Photosynthesis in plants takes carbon dioxide from the atmosphere.
- Microorganisms break down both dead animals and plants and release carbon dioxide into the atmosphere in decomposition.
- Combustion or burning release carbon dioxide from fossil fuels.

7 (a) Some of the mass is lost as waste/faeces/urine (1); some is used in respiration by the tuna fish/some is lost due to output of carbon dioxide (1).
(b) pyramid shape (1); bottom box labelled phytoplankton, next two boxes labelled mackerel and then tuna fish (1)

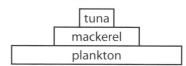

(c) Energy: some stored in body mass in the eater (1); some is lost as heat/used in respiration (1). Carbon, any two from: some carbon ends up in the eater (1); some carbon is lost as carbon dioxide to the atmosphere (1); some carbon ends up in waste (1).

8 Any three from: large feet to stop sinking in sand (1); nostrils that close to stop sand getting in (1); fat store in hump for food/energy (1); long legs to keep away from hot sand (1).

9 When giraffes reproduce the offspring have a variety of neck lengths (1); those with the longest necks can reach the most food (1); and therefore survive to reproduce more often than the shorter-necked ones (1); so more offspring in the next generation have longer necks (1).

10 (a) A: oestrogen (1); B: LH (1); C: FSH (1)
(b) FSH: makes eggs mature in the ovaries OR stimulates the production of oestrogen (1); LA: stimulates the release of eggs from the ovaries (1); oestrogen: stimulates the lining of the womb to build up OR slow down the production of FSH (1).

11 (a) Any two from: a placebo is a tablet with no active drug (1). It is used because sometimes people's health can change if they only think they are being treated (1), so the trial needs to look at the difference between people on the drug and people on a placebo (1).

(b) A double-blind trial is a trial where neither the doctors nor the patients know who is getting the drug and who is getting the placebo (1). It is done so that the doctor and the patient are objective (1). *'Objective' means that the doctor and patients will decide if the drug works based only on evidence, not on what they expect to happen.*

(c) The doctor's decision is right (1); after four years the patients taking the placebo were twice as likely to suffer from heart or circulatory disease (7.6 per 100 rather than 3.8 per 100) (1), so in this study statins help to reduce the likelihood of heart disease (1).

(d) There are a large number of people in this trial (1); this means that the results are more reliable (1).

Science A Chemistry C1 practice paper

1 (a) (i) brass (1) **(ii)** tungsten (1)

(b) The missing data is: 74; 110; 74 (1) and 82; 207 (1)

(c) (i) Argon is unreactive (1), so will not react with the hot filament/air would react with the hot filament (1).

(ii) helium/neon/krypton/xenon/radon (1)

(iii)

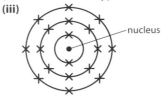

nucleus

completed target diagram with electronic structure 2,8,8 (1)

2 (a) arrow from copper products to impure copper (1)

(b) electrolysis (1)

(c) Phytomining uses plants to extract metals from compounds in the soil (1). The plants are burned to obtain the metal compounds (1).

(d) A basic answer would give a simple description of an advantage **and/or** a disadvantage of recycling different metals.

A good answer would give a clear description of both advantages **and** a disadvantage. Clear references are made to **one or two** of the issues, economic, ethical or environmental.

An excellent answer would give a detailed description of both advantages **and** a disadvantage. References are made to data from the graph and a wide range of issues.

Examples of chemistry points made in the response:

- Advantages of recycling metals: saves ore which may be running out; fewer mines so less pollution; less waste from mining for disposal; usually less energy needed for recycling compared with extracting from ore; extracting ores releases harmful gases, etc.

- Disadvantages of recycling metals: sometimes difficult to separate impurities from metal, etc.

- References to data from table could include: High proportion of lead recycled as ore running out or easy to recycle; low value of tin recycled as its difficult to separate from impurities, etc.

3 (a) 6 molecules of carbon dioxide combine with 6 molecules of water (1) to produce 1 molecule of glucose and 6 molecules of oxygen (1).

(b) They have lots of sugar or they don't have a lot of oil (1).

(c) C_8H_{18} (1)

(d) C_3H_8O (1) and 115 °C +/− 15 °C (1)

4 (a) The gases are cooled and condense (1).

(b) (i) Fraction 5 (1) **(ii)** Fraction 1 (1)

(c) Cracking is carried out to make more of the smaller molecules/fractions (1) which are in greater demand (1).

(d) C_4H_{10} (1)

(e) (i) ethene (1)

(ii) Add bromine water (1); changes from orange/ brown to colourless in C_2H_4 (1).

(iii) plastic/poly(propene)/polymer (1)

5 (a) (i) Its limited availability OR does not work as well as diesel (1).

(ii) The only product is water (1).

(iii) Possible answers include: powder fuel to improve flow/removal of pollutants from fuel/waste gases/improved air flow to ensure complete combustion (1).

(b) increased risk of obesity (1) and heart disease (1)

(c) (i) W and Y (1);

(ii) Z (1)

(d) Advantages: Cornstarch bags do not use up resources of crude oil (1) and cause less pollution when they are thrown away (1). Disadvantage: Cornstarch bags may start to break down too soon (1).

6 (a) (i) at the boundaries between (tectonic) plates (1)

(ii) Earthquakes occur when the plates suddenly move (1).

(b) The carbon dioxide in the atmosphere dissolves in the oceans (1); marine creatures absorb the carbon dioxide (to make shells) (1) and when the shellfish die they become limestone rock (1).

(c) mass of carbon dioxide = 20 − 11.2 (1) = 8.8 g (1)

7 (a) (i) The continents seem to fit together (1) and the same fossils/rocks are found on different continents (1).

(ii) Difference: In Wegener's theory the ocean beds were fixed, in the modern theory parts of the ocean beds move with the continents (1). Similarity: Both had large areas moving in different directions (1).

(b) (i) increasing (1)

(ii) 420 ppm +/− 5 ppm (1)

(iii) Global warming (1) could cause (any two of) climate change; areas of drought; melting of polar ice caps; rising sea levels (2).

Science A Physics P1 practice paper

1 (a) (i) microwave and infrared (both required for 1 mark)

(ii) visible light (1)

(b) Any one from: travel at the same speed in a vacuum (1), can all be reflected (1), they obey the equation $v = f \times \lambda$ (1).

(c) prediction (1); based on scientific evidence (1)

(d) (i) A large sample size allows a relationship to be identified/reduces the effect of anomalous data (1).

(ii) Advantage: using young people could be thought of as ethically wrong (1). Disadvantage: not including children in the study makes it impossible to establish a relationship between cancer in young people/not a valid research study. (1)

2 (a) B – iron (1)
  (b) When 100 joules of energy come into an appliance, 100 joules of energy is converted.
  The energy transferred by an appliance will make the surroundings warmer.
  An electrical appliance that converts 500 J of input energy to 380 J of output energy is 76% efficient (all correct, 2; any two correct, 1).
3 (a) (i) The refracted ray is labelled (1) with it bending towards the normal (1).
  (ii) The reflected ray is correctly labelled (1) with the angle of reflection equal to the angle of incidence (1). *Allow tolerance of 2 degrees.*

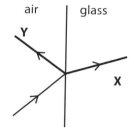

  (b) (i) diffraction (1)
  (ii) The wavelength of the water wave is equal/similar to the gap so diffraction occurs (1). The wavelength of the water wave is much smaller than the gap, so diffraction does not occur (1).
4 (a) coal, oil and natural gas (1)
  (b) lower current (1); less energy loss/wasted as heat (1)
  (c) Advantages: more energy released per kg of fuel (1), does not produce greenhouse gases (1). Disadvantages: produces radioactive waste (1), dangerous if a nuclear accident (1).
  (d) They may be due to decreased supplies/reserves of fossil fuels (1); may be due to environmental issues (1).
5 (a) efficiency = energy output/energy input × 100% = 200 MJ/225 MJ × 100% (1) = 89% (or 0.89) (1).
  (b) 24 MJ = 75 × 4200 × change in temperature (1); change in temperature = 76.2 °C (1); final temperature = 86.2 °C (1)
  (c) (i) 0.8 kW × 5 hours = 4 kWh (1)
  (ii) cost = number of kWh used × cost per kWh = 4 kWh × 12p (1) = 48p (1)
6 (a) 13 squares = 130 J (1)
  (b) 1 square (light energy) + 3 squares (sound energy) = 4 squares = 40 J (1)
  (c) efficiency = useful energy/total energy supplied × 100% (1) = 31% (or 4/13 or 40/130 or 0.31) (1)
7 (a) frequency = velocity ÷ wavelength = 300 000 000 ÷ 1500 (1) = 200 000 Hz (or 200 kHz) (1)
  (b) Any two from: radio waves are transverse and sound waves are longitudinal (1), radio waves can travel in a vacuum, sound waves need a medium to travel through (1), radio waves travel much faster than sound waves (1).
8 (a) (i) There is direct proportionality between speed of a galaxy and its distance from Earth/as the distance of a galaxy from Earth increases, its speed increases (1) (either of these statements for 1 mark).
  (ii) Observed wavelength of dark line from distant galaxy has increased (1), so must be moving away from Earth red-shifted (1); so Universe must be expanding from a small point (1).

  (b) Cosmic Microwave Background Radiation (1); radiation from the Big Bang that is still present and detectable today (1).
9 (a) The direction of vibration of particles is parallel to direction of energy transfer producing a longitudinal wave and sound is a longitudinal wave (1). Springs compressed/compressions represent areas of high pressure (1) in sound wave in air and areas where springs spread out represent rarefactions/areas of low pressure (1) in sound wave in air.
  (b) (i) increases (1)
  (ii) decreases (1)
10 A basic answer would give a brief description of reducing the heat losses from the tank, but would not explain how this is done.
  A good answer would give a clear description of how the heat losses are reduced.
  An excellent answer would give a clear, detailed and balanced description of how the heat losses are reduced.

Examples of physics points made in the response:
- The old tank will transfer heat rapidly to the air by conduction, convection and radiation/The new tank will reduce the amount of heat transferred to the air via lowering the rate of conduction, convection and radiation.
- The existing tank transfers lots of energy to its surroundings by conduction and convection because it has no insulation.
- The new tank will reduce heat transfer by radiation because the inner reflective coating will reflect heat back into the water tank.
- The new tank will reduce heat transfer by radiation because the outer reflective surface is a poor emitter of infrared radiation.
- The new tank will reduce heat loss by convection because the insulating material contains trapped air.
- The new tank will reduce heat transfer by conduction because the insulating material is a poor conductor/reference to vibrations and electrons.
- The homeowner's energy bills will decrease because much less energy is being transferred to the surroundings.
- Much less energy is needed to keep the water in the tank hot.

Published by Pearson Education Limited, Edinburgh Gate, Harlow, Essex, CM20 2JE.

www.pearsonschoolsandfecolleges.co.uk

Copies of official specifications for all AQA qualifications may be found on the AQA website: www.aqa.org.uk

Text and original illustrations © Pearson Education Limited 2013
Edited by Jim Newall and Florence Production Ltd
Typeset and illustrated by Tech-Set Ltd, Gateshead
Cover illustration by Miriam Sturdee

The rights of Iain Brand and Mike O'Neill to be identified as authors of this work have been asserted by them in accordance with the Copyright, Designs and Patents Act 1988.

First published 2013

17 16 15 14
10 9 8 7 6 5 4 3 2

British Library Cataloguing in Publication Data
A catalogue record for this book is available from the British Library

ISBN 978 1 447 94215 3

Printed in Slovakia by Neografia

All images © Pearson Education

In the writing of this book, no AQA examiners authored sections relevant to examination papers for which they have responsibility.